# Symbols Now

Edited by

Chris Abbott

Widgit Software Ltd, Leamington Spa

Widgit Software Ltd
26 Queen Street, Cubbington, Leamington Spa, CV32 7NA

First Published in Great Britain by
Widgit Software Ltd 2000



ISBN 0-9539346-0-8



Typeset by Widgit Software Ltd
Printed in Great Britain by Ashford Colour Press Ltd.

# Contents

# Acknowledgements

Grateful thanks are offered to the Steering Committee for their valuable contribution both during meetings, in planning the book and in reading several drafts, to Meldreth Manor School for hosting the committee meetings and to Tracey Baldwin at Widgit Software for administering the project.

We are indebted to the many professionals who have generously shared their work. We received a great many contributions, too many to include. We have tried to draw a representative collection of examples from those submitted, but extend our grateful thanks to everybody who contributed. A full list of people who submitted material is given in the appendix. We are also grateful to the members of the community who have read drafts of the book and given valuable comment.

This book has been published by Widgit Software, who also produce Writing with Symbols 2000 and have been involved in symbol software for many years. Although many of the case studies relate to the use of this software, the intention of the book is to indicate the range of uses to which symbols are being put; it is the symbol which is our focus and not the software tool.

# Foreword

In March 1999 a symbol conference was held at Meldreth Manor Scope School. At the conference there was a very successful 'bring-and-share' display of work by delegates and the people with whom they work. By the end of the conference it was decided that we should find ways to share practice more widely, to the benefit of everybody working in the symbol field. One suggestion was publication of a book highlighting interesting and good practice which could help inform newcomers and experienced practitioners alike.

The creation of this book was facilitated by a generous grant from the Viscount Nuffield Auxiliary Fund to Meldreth Manor School and Widgit Software Ltd towards the authoring and admisistrative costs.. As part of the project Chris Abbott gathered examples of symbol practice from all over the UK and beyond, collating them in this book. A steering committee, chaired by David Banes, former Head of Meldreth Manor School, advised and Widgit Software provided practical assistance and publication.

Members of the Steering Committee:

David Banes, Director of Operations for Abilitynet (Chair)
Chris Stevens, SEN Manager, BECTa
Bernard Gummett, Head Teacher, George Hastwell School, Barrow-in Furness
Jackie Stubbs, Speech and Language Therapist,New Possibilities NHS Trust
Gela Griffiths, Senior Teacher, Redbridge High School, Liverpool
Tina Detheridge, Director, Widgit Software Ltd
Chris Abbott, School of Education, Kings College, London

# CHAPTER 1

## INTRODUCTION AND BACKGROUND

### Introduction

*Throughout this book the term* ***User*** *has been adopted to denote a symbol reader or writer. This covers the many terms in practice: pupil, student, client service user, centre member. It should be noted that some of the names in this book have been changed for reasons of confidentiality.*

Symbols have been used as part of aided and augmentative communication systems for many years. They are used by people without speech, through communication boards or electronic aids, and to enhance direct face-to-face communication. People without intellectual impairments may use complex systems to obtain access to language through dynamic electronic aids. People with learning difficulties may be better served by simpler aids or communication books enabling them to make known their wants and needs.

More recently, symbols have been used to support written communication: to augment the use of text as a medium for reading and writing. This is particularly valuable for people with severe learning difficulties who may have only a limited sight vocabulary of text. It is this use of symbols that is the particular, although not exclusive, concern of this book.

The word symbol is used throughout the book in a rather loose way to imply any graphic that is used in a communicative sense representing a concept or idea. There is a continuum of types of graphic images, from photographs through to illustrations, and from illustrative drawings to symbolic representation. Most symbol users will draw on one or more of the published symbol sets that are available. In addition they may adopt specific images to meet their personal vocabulary needs.

It is not the intention of this book to discuss these differences in any depth, nor to imply any judgements regarding the different sets and styles. We look instead at the considerable range of ways in which such representations are currently being used to support the education and autonomy of children and adults with learning disabilities. We intend this to be a celebration of the creativity and imagination of the many students, teachers, therapists, parents and carers who have explored the possibilities for their use.

There is no long history upon which to draw, nor is there yet a recognised body of researched good practice. Rather, we are sharing good practice through experience, so that we may learn together. This book draws together a wide range of practices from around the UK and beyond, expressly for this purpose of sharing ideas and developing symbol use.

## Background

The advent of symbol software has had a significant impact on the growth of symbol use, particularly on symbol use to support information and learning. The original tools, Using Rebus, Using Symbols, and From Pictures to Words, were very unsophisticated but did allow the consistent reproduction of images. The power of this was quickly recognised. For example, Curriculum Guidance 9 from the then National Curriculum Council in 1992 recommended the use of symbols. The development of Writing with Symbols, the first 'symbol processor' was helped by support from the Viscount Nuffield Auxiliary Fund, who have also supported the development of this book. The software did not prevent symbols being hand drawn, but facilitated writing by teachers and carers to create symbol supported text by giving an easy way of reproducing symbols. Symbol Users were also able to write with the help of additional devices and utilities such as on-screen grids and overlay keyboards from which they could directly select symbols to go into a document on screen.

What has amazed us all has been the range of applications conceived. The original tools soon seemed limited; the boundaries of their capability were reached, and demand grew for more advanced tools for writing and presentation. With that has come some understanding of the possibilities and limitations of this form of writing, and software development has been informed by practitioners at every stage.

At the same time, socio-linguists (Kress & van Leeuwen, 1996) have become increasingly interested in the whole area of visual literacy. The use of emoticons, punctuation marks, icons on the Internet, has been one focus of attention. Another area of research has been the increasing use of symbolised information in public spaces. This book deals, however, with specific uses of symbols for communication and literacy in the context of supporting people with learning difficulties.

## Symbol sets and styles

It is important to understand the nature and constraints of each type of symbol style, and how each can be used to meet different purposes. At the same time we are starting to consider the linguistic possibilities and constraints of the symbol sets in order that we may choose the most appropriate graphic representations and styles for each user. There are three types of graphic representation, which we will describe here as Pictures, Illustrations and Symbols.

### Pictures

Photographs are easily used in graphic writing, from scanned pictures or by using a digital camera. Photographs are good for indicating specific people, places or things. They are not good, however, for more general communication. It is difficult to clearly draw a single concept from, for instance a photograph of a cat eating from a bowl – is it intending to communicate cat, cat eating, cat food, tabby cat, or my pet cat? However photographs can be used very easily in conjunction with symbols to enhance communication.

### Illustrations

An illustration, like a photograph or detailed picture, will contain quite a lot of information. It will provide good support for a concept, so may well illustrate a whole sentence or idea. For example, many health education leaflets would communicate the information more easily through the use of illustrations rather than by a linguistically structured series of symbols. A drawing will be more general, communicating perhaps the idea of a woman, rather than a specific woman. There is likely to be a facial image which could communicate attitude, at the same time as showing a particular procedure or action. Illustrations may be very good at conveying information. They are not so good for constructing graphic supported text, or for a disabled person learning to write. The example below shows how an illustration can enhance symbol or text communication.

*Illustrations give different types of information from symbols.*

Put your arms around the body.

## Symbols

A symbol is intended to convey a single idea or concept. Often a symbol is linked to a single word or double word relating to a single idea. Within the range of symbols there are those which are transparent or guessable, such as most nouns and many verbs. There are also those which are translucent or learnable; these may not be immediately recognisable, but the link between the image and its referent can be understood after explanation and remembered. The third category are opaque symbols. These cannot normally be represented by anything other than an entirely abstract, and possibly arbitrary, image and these have to be learned. They are not necessarily required at all levels of communication.

**Transparent or guessable symbols:**

*Symbols that are often easily recognised by non-symbol users.*

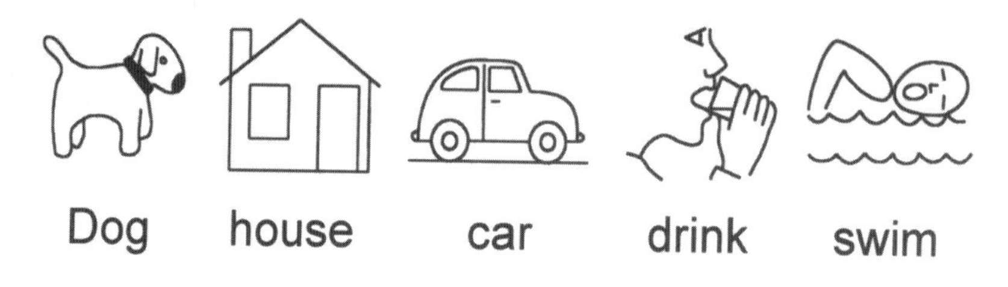


**Translucent or learnable symbols:**

*Symbols that can be learned. Symbols which fit into groups or 'schema'.*

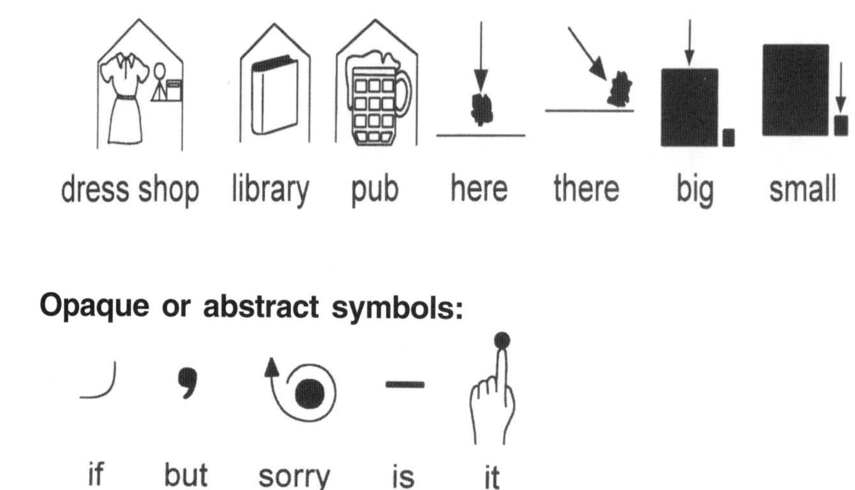


### Symbol sets

The types of symbols used by people with learning disabilities tend to fall into a loose category of pictorial symbols. They are essentially illustrative in nature, although they have some underlying logic which allows a degree of grammatical use. The extent of the grammatical elements varies from set to set. The symbols which are transparent are likely to be similar from one set to another. The difference is stylistic rather than fundamental.

There has been much debate about whether users should have a single symbol style, which is rigidly adhered to within the locality or even nationally, as opposed to a pragmatic eclectic range. There are no researched answers to these questions. It appears from practice that some users will require a particular style while others, perhaps those who are more familiar with symbol writing, will be able to work with a mixed or personally-tailored approach.

*Guessable symbols from different symbol sets.*

In addition, there are some design considerations: in the same way that a document written in many mixed fonts can be hard to read and visually confusing, so a page of very mixed images may be less aesthetically pleasing than a page of similar style symbols. However, it can be argued that it is better to have at least some symbol where needed than stick rigidly to a single collection and have blanks in the visual communication. The general consensus seems that it is better to adhere to one style as far as possible, at least for a single user or organisation, and organisations are constructing their own vocabulary sets based around their preferred option, but filling gaps from other sets. More research is needed on the whole field of symbol recognition, preferences and tolerances.

## Preparing symbol supported information

As more symbol supported material is being prepared for organisational and public use, care needs to be taken so that the information is the most effective for the intended audience. The main considerations in preparing symbol supported material are:

- the level or complexity of the message;
- whether the material is to be read independently or if it is to be mediated;
- the types of images to be used – photographs, illustrations or symbols; and
- the relationship between the symbol and any text equivalent. This is especially important when considering written information that is created for a graphic reader, i.e. somebody familiar with symbols who can read the graphic message.

## Users and purposes

Symbols are being used in a great variety of contexts: in the home, in schools and colleges to support communication and education, in day centres and residential homes to facilitate independence, in the workplace to increase participation.

The following six chapters show how this is being realised in practice. They draw out some of the themes and issues relating to symbol use, identifying some of the unanswered questions about symbols, their nature and their application.

The following chapters look at:

2 A range of purposes for which symbols are being used.

3 The difficult and complex issue of consistency within symbol use and the vocabulary to be symbolised.

4 The important issue of communication, where symbols are a lifeline for many users.

5 Symbols for accessing information.

6 The extent to which the use of symbols can assist inclusion, within educational and other settings.

7 Literacy and literature within schooling and beyond

8 The conclusion brings together some of the common overriding themes from each chapter and suggests possible directions of investigation for future development and research.

# CHAPTER 2

## SYMBOLS FOR DIFFERENT PURPOSES

**The use of symbols in daily life serves a broad range of purposes. This chapter illustrates the variety of purposes and contexts.**

**Symbols are used in schools to enhance communication and learning, They are used in residential and day environments to make it safer for people who live or visit there, and to help them feel included in the management of their centre.**

**Families who have young children with communication difficulties, or lifelong symbol users, can use symbols in inventive ways to maintain communication and build family relationships. Symbols can also provide a lifeline to families where a member has suddenly lost the power of speech.**

➤ In Johanna Frohm's family, symbols have made a big difference to the quality of life of her adult son, and have helped to maintain strong family links. Johanna has used symbols to prepare a family history book.

*The mixture of symbols and photographs gives a clear record of events.*

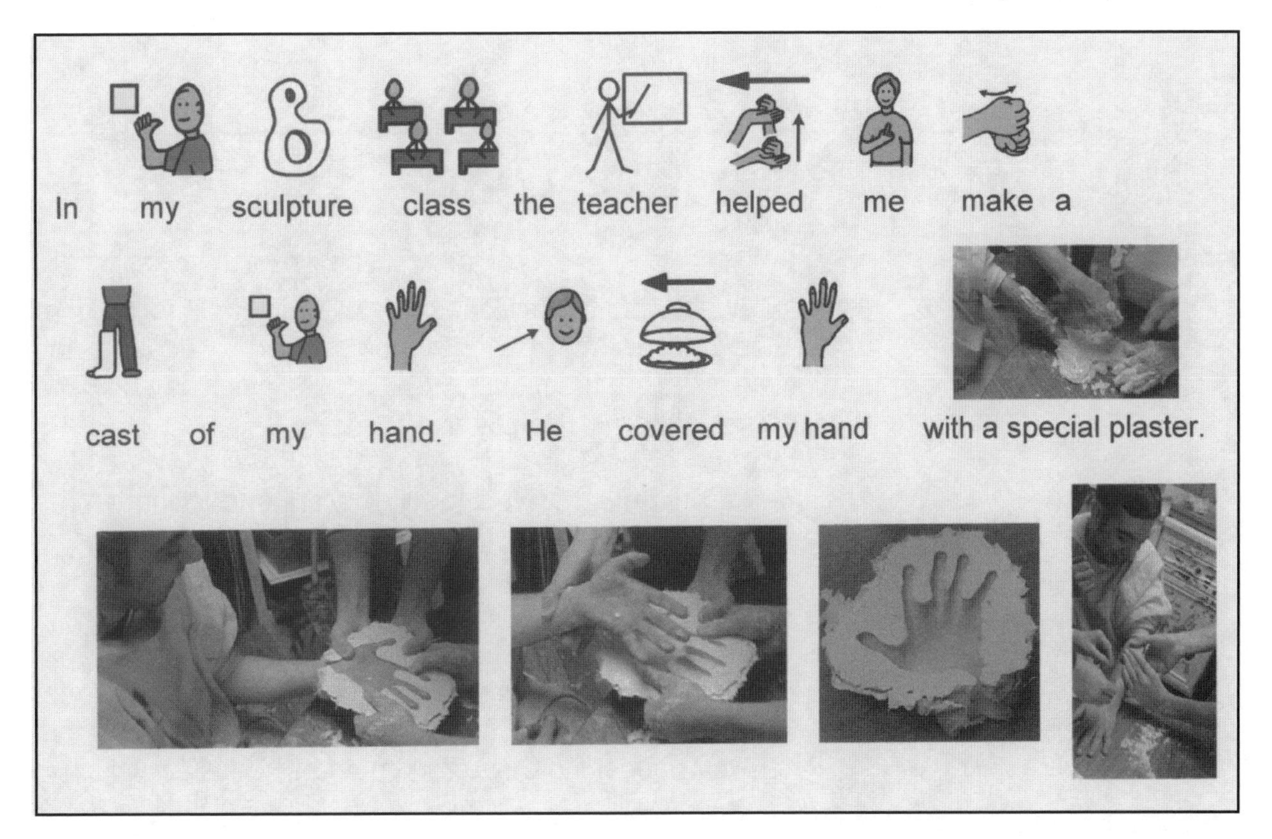

The book is in the form of a collection of photographs, stories and family trees, the latter being produced by a genealogical program. The stories are written in symbols and each is three to five pages long, using symbols, text and scanned photographs. Pictures of Mike with the people described were included as often as possible and the stories were condensed or details eliminated so that they would be understandable to him.

The book was built up in stages with Mike being given part of it at a time and it now offers a resource not only for him but for his carers.

> 'The family trees help them to identify family members who correspond with our son but who do not live in our community. Also it was pointed out that after our deaths this gives our son something about his family.'

Their use of symbols and the symbol software is now quite sophisticated. Sometimes Johanna does the writing under Mike's guidance. However, she has also set up grids of symbols for Mike to use at home covering a range of activities about things he might want to communicate.

*A set of grids that have vocabulary for one adult to write freely about family, friends and events. This grid grows each time it is used.*

| Support | Family | Friends | More friends | Family friends | Arnold Center people | Arnold Center Work |
|---|---|---|---|---|---|---|
| more work | school | night school | recreation | Places | travel | weather |
| animal | Say | Entertainment | Restaurant | Su M T W Th F Sa Week | Month | |
| Health | Body | feelings | Store | Food | | Print |

Johanna has set up twenty-one grids with symbols for Mike to use. She uses Writing with Symbols 2000 to do this and particularly likes the function key F11 facility which can be used to reassign or add words to symbols.

The grids are used by Mike's family, carers and teachers in a variety of ways.

Johanna explains:

> 'Together, Mike and his support staff or I will write a letter to a family member, thank you notes or stories about special happenings. His grandmothers frequently write him

> a letter when they receive his letters. It is a way he can correspond with others - and he actively participates in what is written. Frequently before a sentence is completely typed, he has an idea of what else we should include or who else he wants to write to. He and a staff person wrote a story about delays due to fog during his trip to the airport to get a friend. Another story was about a major snowstorm and trying to deliver the newspapers on his paper route. Sometimes he takes the stories to school or work to share with his teacher, supervisor and friends.'

The function key F12 facility in Writing with Symbols allows users to cycle through alternative symbols for a particular word. This is useful for carers and teachers to prepare materials. It can be used by symbol users also, as Johanna explains;

> 'We were writing about the trip to the airport and the flight delays. Two girls were playing. Initially, when I typed "play" the symbol showed a theatre production. Mike commented, "Oh, oh." He knew the symbol was not correct. By pressing F12, we cycled through the other symbols available for play. It was decided the sign language symbol for "play" was most appropriate, since Mike uses some sign language and uses the sign for play.'

Johanna has set up a website which describes how she uses symbols with her son
(http://www.concentric.net/~jdfrohm/symbols.html).

This site describes in detail one family's journey through symbol communication, from the early use of books of Pictorial Communication Symbols (PCS) photocopied to make books, to the discovery of Writing with Symbols 2000 which Johanna found after searching the Web for a Windows program offering text, symbols and speech and which Mike could use independently.

This process of creating the family history book is also described on her website at http://www.concentric.net/~jdfrohm/familyhistory.html and in a third section of the website, Johanna passes on some useful tips and advice about symbol use. In particular, there is advice here about using a start-up environment so that a client can access the program independently, as well as the use of single and multiple grids. All of this can be found at http://www.concentric.net/~jdfrohm/tips.html. Johanna has pioneered some of this work in the US, and her website is an excellent example and valuable resource for other families.

## Using symbols to assist learning

➤ Peter provides an unusual example of the use of symbols to help a person who can read. He has an autistic spectrum disorder and is hyperlexic. He is a very fluent reader but although he is able to read anything, even very complex material, he has no understanding of what the words mean. Staff at his school added symbols to his texts, from which he has been able to learn what the text is about and to begin to read with some understanding. It is difficult to envisage any other way in which Peter might be taught to read with understanding.

*Symbols supporting the curriculum for an FE student.*

➤ Symbols can be used to support learning in almost every area of the curriculum. A student at Dilston College wrote the recipes below and then added them to her curriculum resource materials.

macaroni cheese and tuna bake

Ingredients

1 lb butter 1 1/2 oz flour 15 fl oz milk 8oz cheese 1 tin of tuna 2 teaspoons
mustard salt and pepper 2 tomatoes

Method

1. cook the macaroni in boiling salted water for 8 to 10 minutes.
2. melt the butter in a saucepan stir in the flour and make a smooth paste.
3. slowly add the milk and mix.
4. Bring to the boil
5. add the cheese the mustard the tin of tuna salt and pepper and cook until the cheese has melted and the sauce is thick and smooth.
6. Drain the macaroni and put it in an ovenproof dish
7. pour over the sauce and stir to mix.
8. arrange the tomato slices on top sprinkle over some cheese and bake at 180c for 15 to 20 minutes.
9. Eat.

➤ Sue Norton teaches science to pupils with moderate learning difficulties. She has worked with Widgit Software to produce a comprehensive set of symbols to support the science national curriculum for key stages 1, 2 and 3. She believes that the pictorial nature of symbols helps the students to recall the concepts.

> 'Symbols appeared to be very effective in enabling recall of information which pupils had previously been unable to remember when asked verbally. Symbols may be successful in enabling correct recall since they are able to convey a lot of information pictorially. In many situations the information embedded in the symbol will be sufficient

to enable the correct recall of the meaning of the word. Many of the science symbols have been specifically designed to reinforce the link between the word and the concept related to it.'

*An extract from the revision notes of Sue Norton's GCSE students. The symbols have had a significant impact on achievement.*

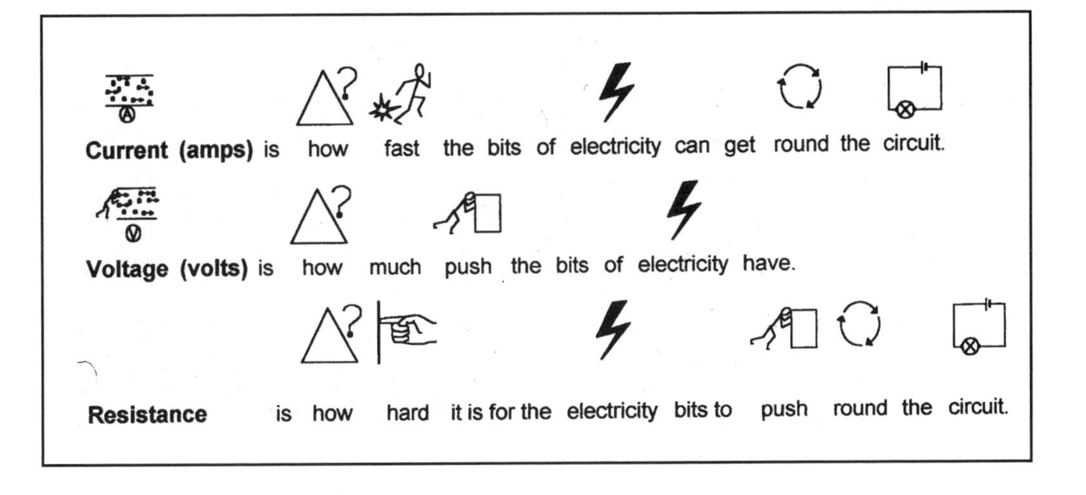


## Group work

➤ Elleray Park School in the Wirral, like many other schools, celebrates World Book Day each year. Symbols were used by Class 3 to write a book describing what happened on that day so students could talk about it later and remember what went on. The book contains a series of A4 photographs of events with a facing page containing a sentence of text and appropriate symbols.

*A book recording a specific whole school event acts as a reminder for participants and contributes to the historical record of the school.*

The school is a totally symbol-based environment, a digital camera has been used to make story books such as 'The Three Little Pigs.' There are three different versions of this story, each with photographs of different children acting it out. Makaton signs are also printed out in the symbol software to extend the use of signing by staff and volunteers, and the school is exploring the use of sound by using .WAV files with Writing with Symbols and Switchit Maker.

They hope to explore this further with children with profound and multiple learning difficulties. In addition, pupils in the school help write their own reading books. Three Pigs and the Big Bad Wolf is written collaboratively by a group of pupils, re-telling the traditional story with additions. It uses a mixture of Rebus and PCS Symbols and photographs of themselves enacting roles. The children built and painted scenery for some of the scenes, and dressed up to act the story. Photographs from this were used in the story. They also chose their own names for the pigs in the story. Personalising the characters clearly helped the children to engage in the process.

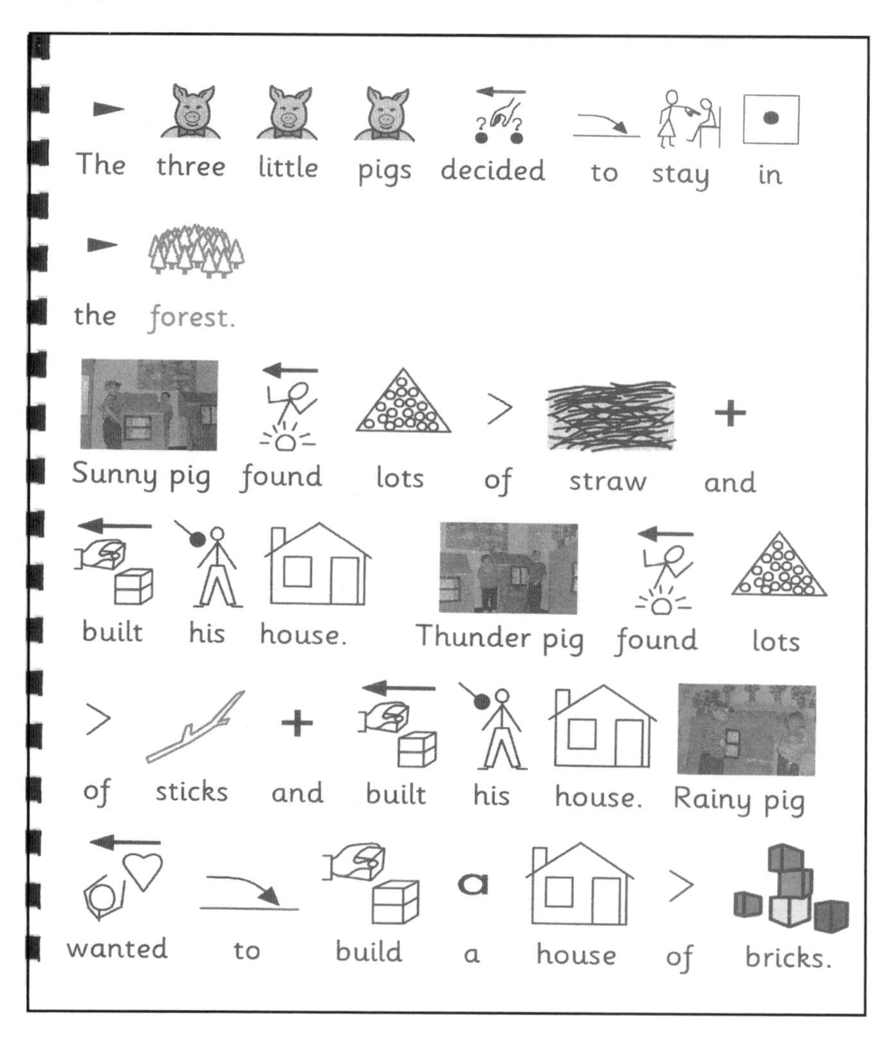


*Collaborative writing by a group of pupils.*

## Using symbols with adults

➤ Many adults are symbol users for a whole host of different reasons. Karen Burton is a Community Education Tutor in Torbay, Devon. She works at Hollacombe Community Resource Centre, a day centre for adults with learning disabilities. Karen has been working with symbols for eight years and uses them at various levels. For her least able clients, symbols are a written form of communication; for the more able they are used to teach reading skills. Within this range of use, symbols can be found at the resource centre in timetables, menus, minutes of clients' committee meetings, newspapers, signs, publicity and labels. Symbolised texts such as timetables make use of small digitised photographs of people who are associated with each activity, so a picture of one of the staff will appear next to that person's session.

*Materials developed for adults by resource centres.*

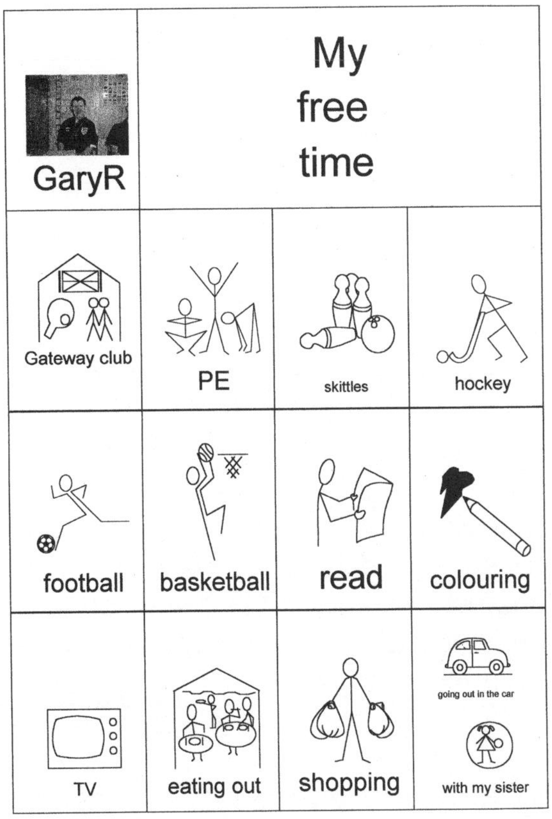

| GaryR | My free time | | |
|---|---|---|---|
| Gateway club | PE | skittles | hockey |
| football | basketball | read | colouring |
| TV | eating out | shopping | going out in the car<br>with my sister |

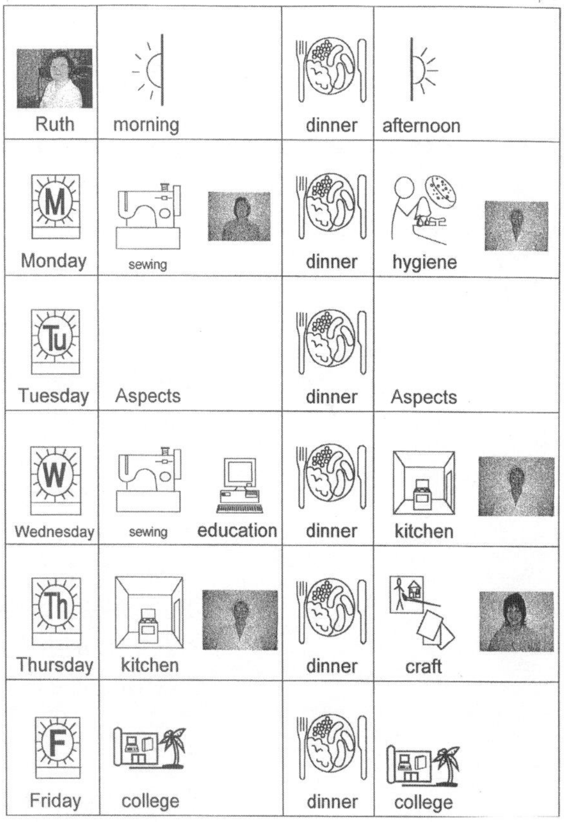

| Ruth | morning | dinner | afternoon |
|---|---|---|---|
| Monday | sewing | dinner | hygiene |
| Tuesday | Aspects | dinner | Aspects |
| Wednesday | sewing education | dinner | kitchen |
| Thursday | kitchen | dinner | craft |
| Friday | college | dinner | college |

➤ Anne Hancox also works with adult clients, in both day centres and residential homes. Having been involved with symbols for over twenty years, Anne has a wealth of experience to share. She uses symbols for basic communication with people who have limited verbal skills. She makes charts, communication books and swatches as well as communication aids. For people with limited reading skills, Anne uses symbols to label the doors of rooms and cupboards, to display safety warnings and list rules. She also worked with the fire prevention officer to produce a fire notice in symbol form.

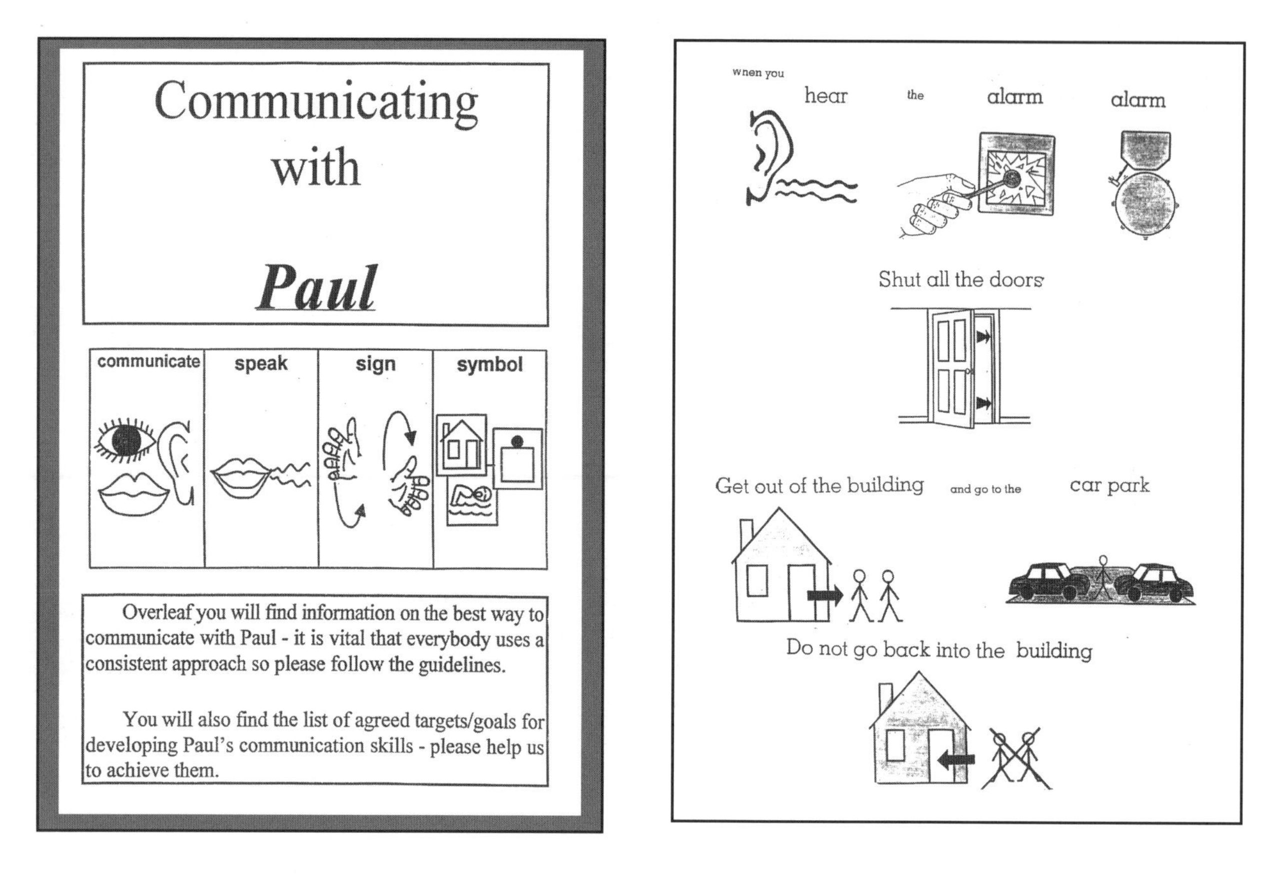


*Symbol materials can help staff and users to work together.*

Symbolised timetables are used to reduce frustration and subsequent behaviour problems caused by inability to predict events. Sequenced sets of symbols are used to prepare clients for visits to the hospital or dentist. The symbols show the different people and actions that will take place. The visual clues are more easily remembered than a set of verbal instructions. Symbols are also used in rehearsal games, and games that practice basic skills. Lotto, for example is a popular game, and symbolised alternatives allow nonverbal clients to join.

## Supporting learning at home as well as in school.

➤ Miles and Abigail both have Joubert's Syndrome, a genetic condition which is similar to Cerebral Palsy. The condition causes gross and fine motor control problems, and their speech is also affected. They both attend a school for children with severe learning difficulties. Symbols are used at the school throughout the curriculum. As well as curriculum work, the Writing with Symbols software enables Miles and Abigail to share their news and weekend activities with others much more easily. Using symbols gives both of them a sense of security and the knowledge that what they are typing is correct, as they can check which symbol appears.

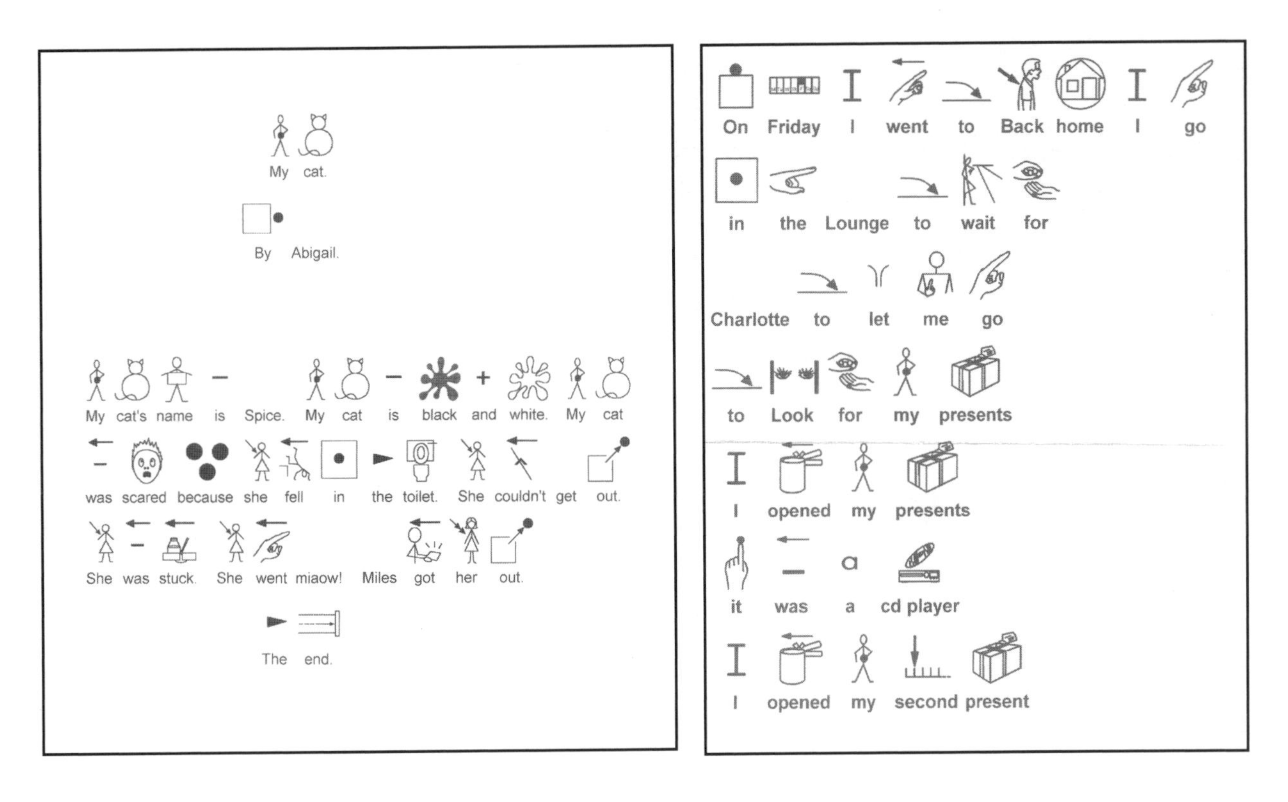


Eventually, it is hoped, they will move to text processing, but at the moment Miles and Abigail very much enjoy writing with symbols and are very reluctant to return to a simple word processing program.

*Symbols can help to overcome motor difficulties, and to motivate writers who find difficulty writing.*

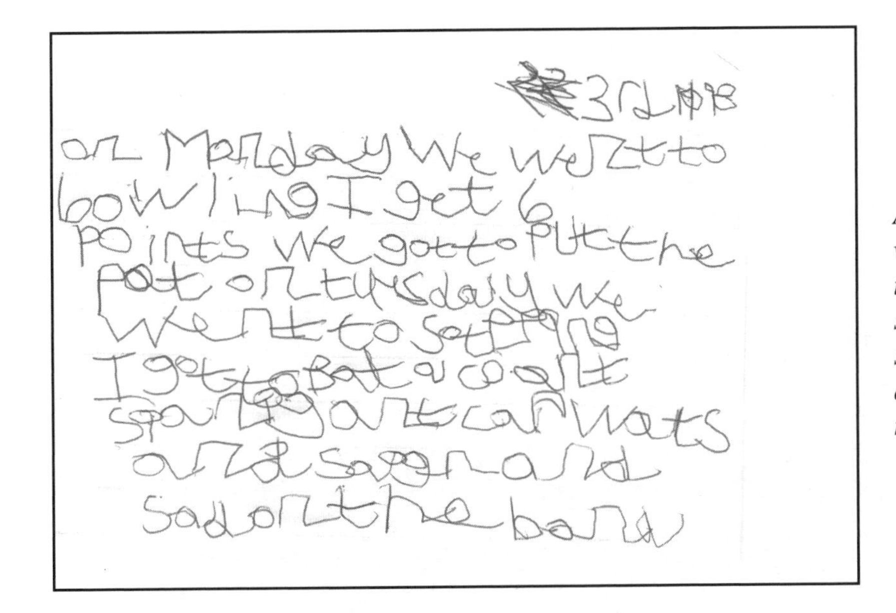

*A piece of handwriting written by the same child as the above symbol print. The symbols reinforce the meaning so that both the child and the adults are sure of the meaning.*

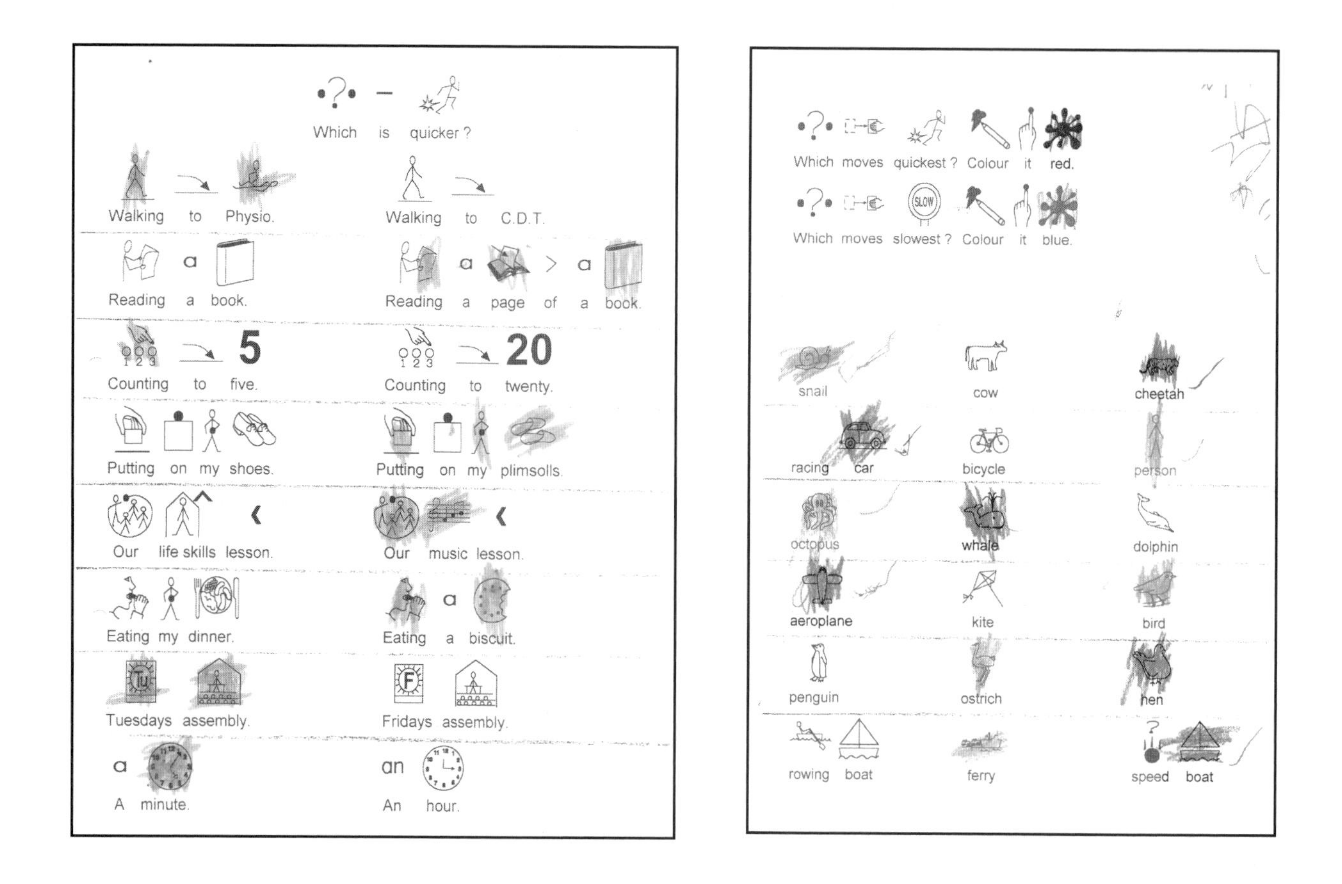


The symbols on these worksheets allow the pupils to demonstrate cognition without being restricted by either their text competence or any difficulty with their motor skills.

*Symbols can make reading and comprehension easier during lessons.*

➤ As the mother of a nine year old boy with autism, Susan Burnes knows that her son does not have generalised learning difficulties but what she describes as 'severe communication difficulties.' He has adapted very well to symbol use and they are now used both at home and at school to extend his language and literacy. His success with Rebus symbols has given him the confidence to start speaking, and he now utters single words.

Symbols used for his home timetable

Stuart uses this every day at mealtimes to encourage him to request verbally & to use 2 words together. He touches the pictures & says the words. This has been very successful.

He follows the TEACCH approach at school, (TEACCH is Treatment and Education of Autistic and related Communication Handicapped CHildren ). TEACCH advocates the provision of visual cues to support activities, and Writing with Symbols is used at home to support this. There are stand-up names on the dining table, food request cards to encourage him to pair words, home timetables, a washing schedule to provide structure to his days and a recipe sheet for baking, which he enjoys.

*Some of the language learning materials that Susan has created.*

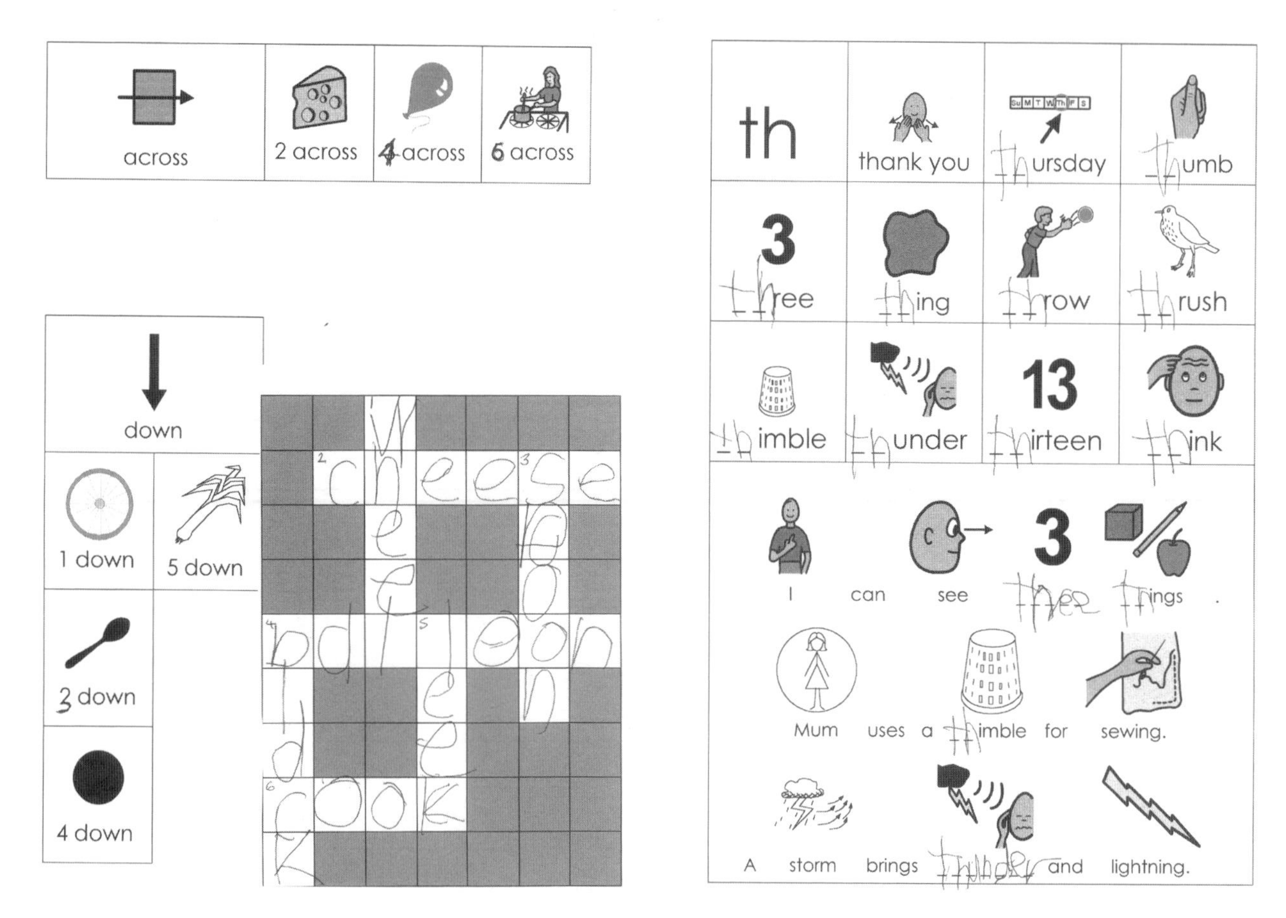


*Different styles of language learning materials can reinforce new vocabulary.*

His mother describes him as now learning to read at home, using a symbol-based approach which she has devised. Susan aims to develop a wider range of symbol vocabulary and grids in future, and the family intends to buy a scanner so that personalised symbols can be added to the wordlist.

## Symbols as a lifeline - particularly within the family

➤ Many people use symbols in the home as part of family life. They may do so because a family member is a lifelong symbol user, or because circumstances have changed and symbols have now become needed. A school or day centre introducing a user to symbols may find that they are also useful to the family. This happened in the unit for pupils with autistic spectrum disorders at Mandeville School in west London, where symbols were used to create a daily activity diary for the students in the group. The symbols were printed onto laminated card and attached with velcro to a strip mounted near each child's desk. As each activity was complete, it was ripped off the velcro day strip and put away. This denoted the passing of each activity, reinforcing the structure of each day. This has been so successful that several of the families of these children now follow the same routine at home.

Some home users have devised ways of using symbols that could be valuable to others, and often these are shared on Websites.

Others have experimented with different materials and books for storing symbols. All have learnt from practical experience about what works and what does not.

➤ Rebecca, another user of symbols, is 18. She attends a school for pupils with severe learning difficulties, and also goes to college once a week. She has also completed some work experience at the Royal Society for the Protection of Birds (RSPB). Her interests range from watching the birds in her garden to RAF aircraft, especially the Vulcan. Language and communication have always presented difficulties for Rebecca, and she has been helped in this area by Judy Melland, her Speech and Language Therapist. Rebecca can be understood by her parents and sister through her use of gesture and body language but people who do not know her find this much more difficult. She uses Makaton signing to help her communicate but her poor co-ordination means that her signs are not always precise enough to be understood.

Rebecca's family decided to try using symbols as she often became frustrated when people did not understand her. Her mother, Wendy, made a book with photographs accompanied by symbols. These were put into a small photograph album which would easily fit into a pocket which she could manage. Initially people tended to think they were being shown photographs and would hand the book back, so the first page says 'Please have patience and look what I want to say.'

*A page from Rebecca's new communication book with prompts about her family and recent holiday.*

| I | we | went | to | Norfolk Broads N | windmills | Tea Rooms | Farm Show |
|---|---|---|---|---|---|---|---|
| Mum | Dad | on | with | Yarmouth Y | racing | big boats | pub |
| Sarah | Grandad | saw | loves | Cromer C | crab | penny machines | fish & chips |
| Pam | Heather | and | in | Stalham S | Kingfisher | Stuart | Jane |

She always carries a photograph album about with her, and she uses this to introduce herself and give important details about her family and interests. There are categories of symbols in the book for all Rebecca's interests so that she can tell others about these. She has extra symbol books for holidays and Christmas. The first book soon became worn as it was used every day and taken everywhere. It had to be continually replaced until the family changed to a ring binder with laminated pages which are much more hard-wearing.

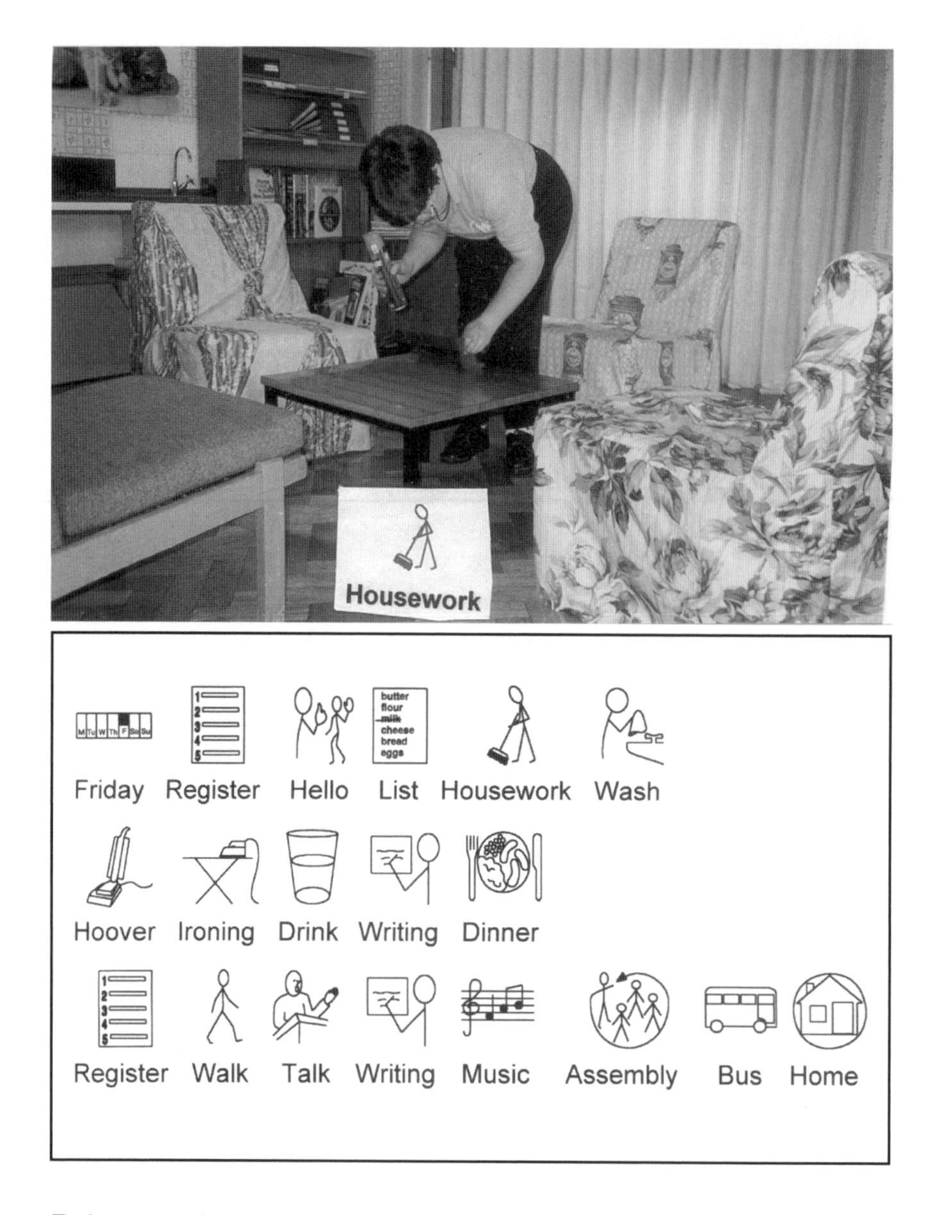


*Opposite pages from Rebecca's communicaiton folder. The photograph gives a lot of additional information to stimulate conversation.*

Rebecca also uses a communication device to develop her language use. This has proved useful but its weight makes it difficult for her to carry it everywhere; portability has been one of the major benefits of the symbol book. Over the two and a half years during which she has been a symbol user Rebecca has developed her concentration, sequencing skills and symbol recognition, and the symbol book has helped avoid frustration caused when she was unable to communicate. It has significantly increased the number of people with whom Rebecca can communicate easily, and she is now beginning to write with symbols. She even has a pen friend.

➤ The Mulholland family work closely with the school at which their son is a day pupil. Symbol diaries are kept, events are planned and shopping lists made – i.e. most things which are done usually with a pen and paper. They find symbols particularly useful for clarifying information and complementing British Sign Language (BSL) vocabulary The family also uses symbols to tell stories. They are starting to use symbols in communication between families as well as with school.

Anne McLellan in Canada uses Writing with Symbols with Graham, her 9 year old non-speaking son with autism. A lot of family photos have been added to the wordlist and the vocabulary for a story about summer camp experiences. Graham's story can be seen on his mother's website at http://www.challengenet.com/~onemom/, along with a comprehensive selection of advice and links for other parents dealing with children within the autistic spectrum disorder.

## Supporting older people with acquired communication problems

➤ When someone suffers a stroke they may lose the ability to speak, at least for a period of time. This is what happened to Ros Chapman's father-in-law. A stroke deprived him of speech so Ros contacted the local nursing staff to see if they thought a communication book would be of benefit to him. Ros knows about symbols as she works as an adviser on issues of special educational needs and Information and Communications Technology, ICT.

The hospital staff readily agreed and explained the things they would like her father-in-law to be able to communicate, such as needing to go to the toilet. Ros started a book written in first person, with an introduction to who he was and explaining what the book was designed to do. The following pages included pictures of his grandchildren and described where they lived. All the pages were made of card (easier to turn over than paper) and put into plastic ring-binder sleeves to protect them.

*A communication book to help an adult in hospital after a stroke.*

Each of the symbol pages contained six symbols and the sentence to which they referred, with the first page containing symbols for tired, lonely, frightened, in pain, thirsty and hungry. The next included requests for a drink or another pillow and so on. The following pages were answers to the sort of questions visitors would ask, for example whether the doctor was coming tomorrow, and how he was feeling that day.

Ros's father-in-law was absolutely delighted with the book and so were the hospital staff – although once he had made himself understood he was so proud of the book that he insisted that his wife take it home to look after it. Luckily, he regained his speech very quickly, but the symbols book helped him to retain some dignity in a difficult situation.

Thank you for coming to see me.

Not everyone who loses the capacity for communication through speech can look forward to its return. James Wright uses symbols at home to help his wife, who has Alzheimer's Disease and has lost the ability to communicate through other forms of language. The couple use symbols at particular times of the day such as meal times and bedtimes, and James recognises that, over time, symbols may become their only means of communication. It can be difficult for people not within educational settings to find out about new ideas and it is heartening to see such help being offered. In this case it was a work experience student attached to the community psychiatric nurse team who helped James to discover what symbols have to offer.

## Summary

Symbols can provide a record of events, aiding recollection.

Symbols can be used in adult settings to aid safety and to promote autonomy.

Symbols can be used to help people with learning difficulties engage in decision making.

Sequences of symbols can illustrate a series of events, which may prepare them for future and possibly stressful events.

Symbols can be a lifeline to families in maintaining communication and building relationships.

By working together, families and other agencies can help symbol users communicate more effectively.

# CHAPTER 3

## SYMBOLS: VOCABULARY, CONSISTENCY AND UNDERSTANDING

**When symbols are used consistently in various environments, such as in a school or a care setting, they are more beneficial to individual users' understanding. Liaison between primary and secondary schools often assists in overcoming complications when users make the transition between the two phases of schooling. This is also helpful for young people when they are preparing to leave school, where symbols can provide information about the numerous options available such as further education or employment.**

**Several schools and centres have found that a more personalised style or modification of existing symbol sets is better suited to some users, even the creation of a whole new style. In this respect symbols may not have fixed meanings and may convey different messages to different users.**

**It is often difficult to determine if a user actually understands symbols or is acting on recall of what has happened earlier. This is true especially where several symbols are available, so careful choice aids understanding. When using symbols to communicate, it is the teacher's or carer's responsibility to check the user's understanding.**

➤ Jackie Stubbs, is aware of the power of symbols in her work as a speech and language therapist. She uses them in a wide variety of contexts, whether computer-generated or produced in other ways. Recently Jackie collaborated on a project with Wendy, a young woman who lives at a social services hostel and attends a supported work place where she works in a greenhouse and a shop. Wendy uses an extensive range of manual signs to communicate very effectively. Over the past seven years she has used symbols for a wide range of functional activities in social and work situations as well as to support her language learning in communication groups run by the local speech and language therapy team. Makaton and Rebus symbols are used within Wendy's work and home situations whenever possible and this maintains continuity with the local schools and consistency with other local services.

Wendy had the opportunity to attend a course based on 'The Health of the Nation' which aimed at exploring all aspects of personal care, dress and health. It was Wendy's first opportunity to participate in an adult learning situation and she was able to actively take part and express her ideas through signing. The other students were able to contribute their ideas through speech, supported by signs, but only a few could read the discussion notes and subsequent session handouts.

Wendy was very proud of her course folder but without symbols she was unable to read it so she agreed to work with Jackie Stubbs, speech and language therapist, on a project to symbolise the course handouts. After each session Jackie provided paper copies of any symbols from existing symbol sets that seemed relevant to the topic. Wendy chose the ones that she felt expressed her ideas best. In many cases the existing symbols were limited and did not really convey the ideas well, therefore new symbols were created usually based on existing symbols but to Wendy's design. In some cases a speech and language therapy assistant created totally new symbols and these were approved by Wendy before being used in the document.

*Examples of symbols designed for Wendy.*

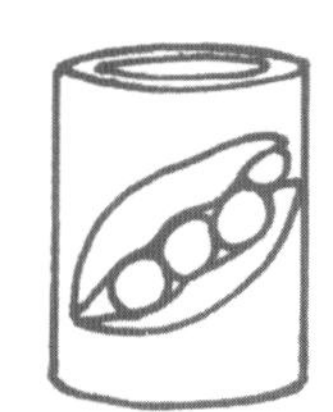

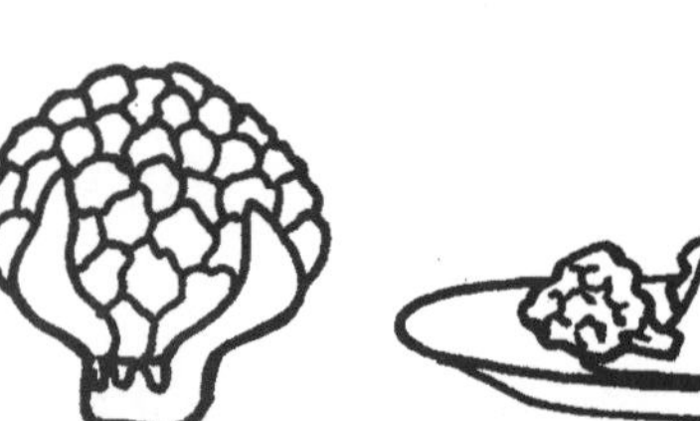

**Dirty teeth** **Peas tinned.** **Cauliflower and cheese sauce.**

**Smells nice** **Looks fit** **Shaves under their arms** **Takes care of their feet**

The final documents contained a mixture of symbols from different published sets as well as individually designed pictorial symbols.

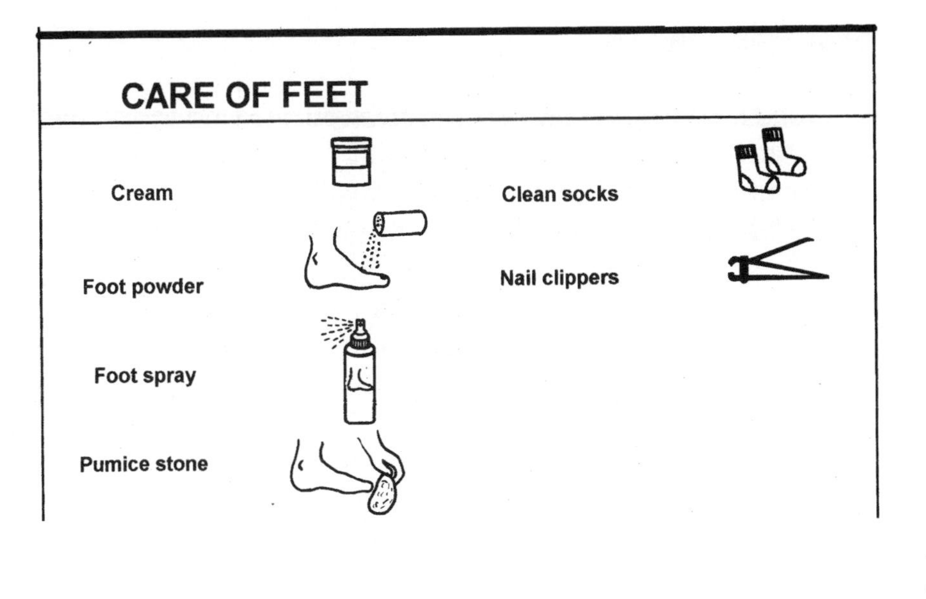


*Examples of symbols from one of the Hygiene Topic Sheets.*

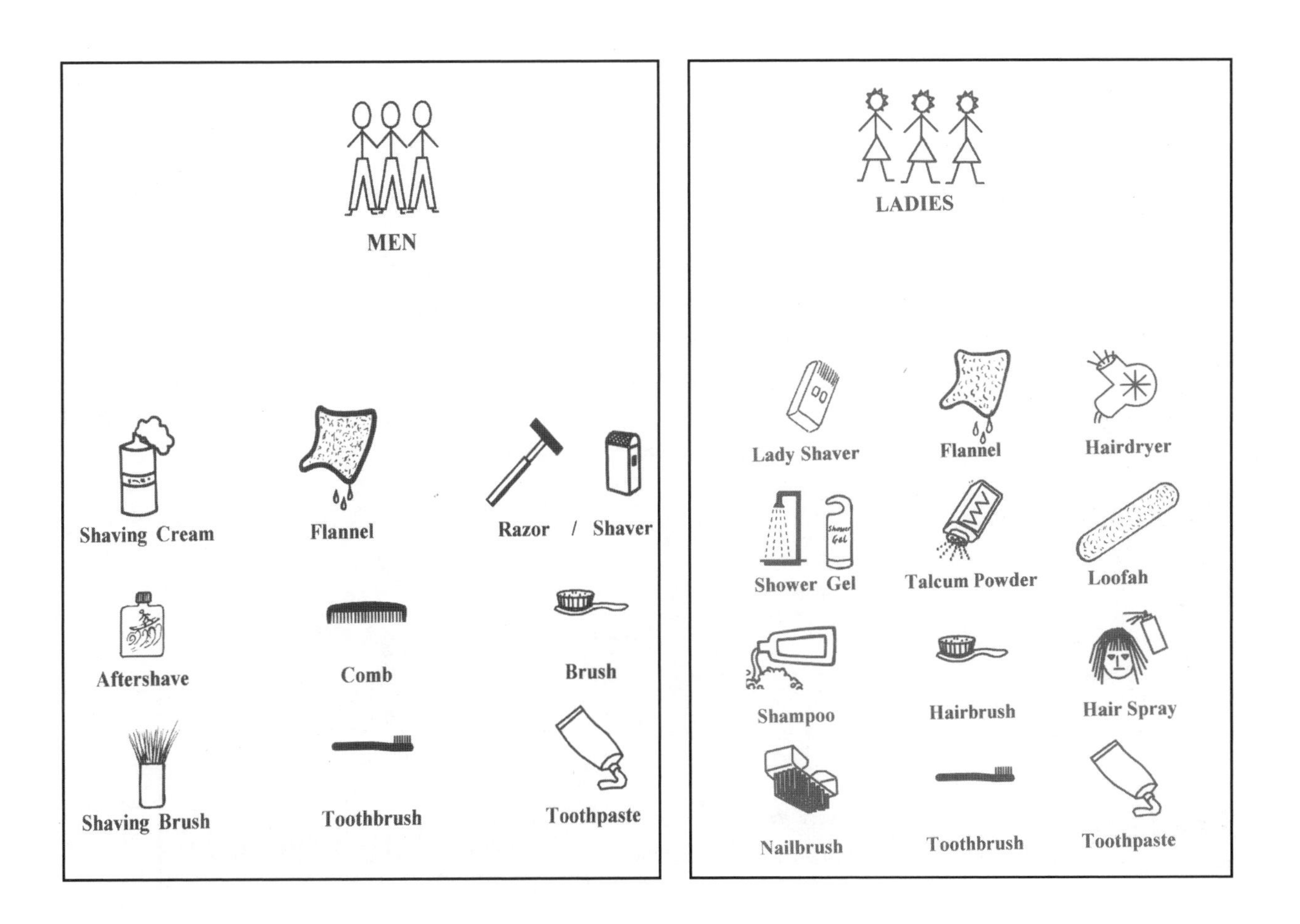


As far as possible consistent design themes and line weights were used throughout to maintain a consistent style. Where abstract symbols were used, these were always taken from the Makaton vocabulary as they were the most familiar to Wendy and her peer group.

## What Was Learned

- Wendy and Jackie only became involved once the course had already started. However, had symbols been used from the outset they would have helped facilitate discussion and feedback for the whole group, not only for one person.

- The layout of the project was determined by the format of the written notes. However, symbols and the graphic layout could have been used more imaginatively to help convey the information.

- Factual information was easily expressed using iconic symbols but more abstract ideas about the course content and ground rules were difficult to express. Concepts such as 'Respect' and 'Confidentiality' are difficult to explain both in symbols and verbally. The use of symbols from the start might also have led to the use of simpler language.

- The process of providing paper copies of the relevant symbols for Wendy's approval was time-consuming. A laptop with a comprehensive range of the available symbols would have solved this problem and given Wendy immediate feedback.

- Wendy chose the symbols that were the most meaningful for her or which appealed to her sense of humour and the final document is therefore very personal to Wendy. The consistent use of abstract symbols from a familiar vocabulary meant that the information was still reasonably accessible to others and reduced the need to learn new symbols.

*A symbol sheet about choosing clothes suitable to wear to a party.*

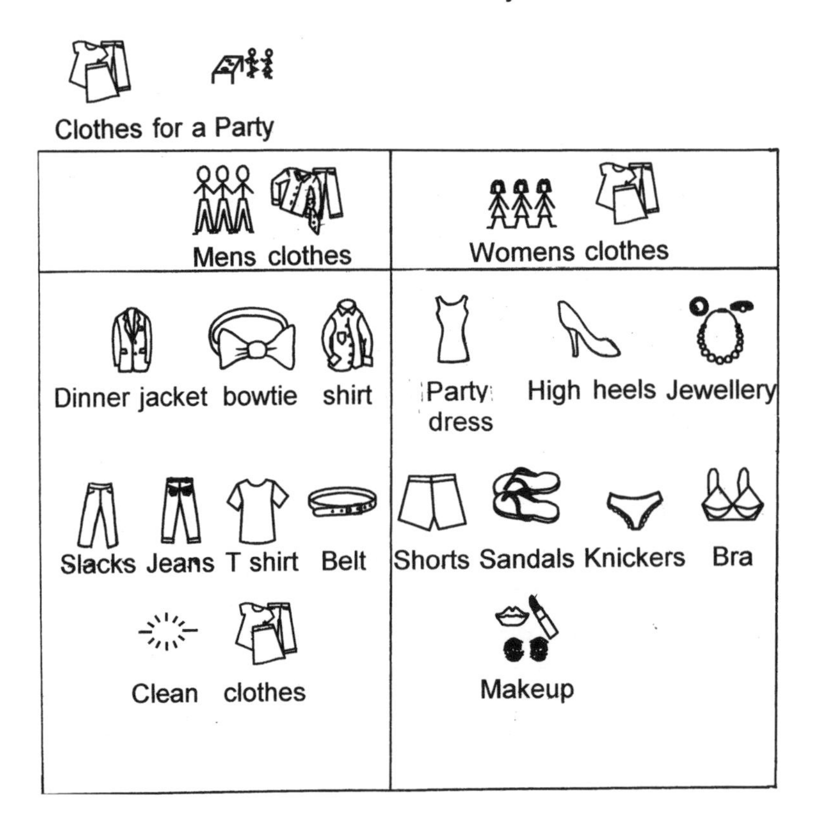

## Dealing with continuity and consistency

Transition from one educational phase to another is a key area for symbol use. There are inevitably tensions between a user's familiarity, and therefore personal continuity, and the 'house styles' commonly used in different environments, thus affecting consistency. The right of the individual to be offered the symbol that means most to them needs to be balanced with local communication systems. It is a challenge to get this right.

➤ Gela Griffiths teaches at Redbridge High School in Liverpool. The school has made the use of symbols an integral part of their English policy. Symbols are used across the whole school - all age groups, classes, subjects, and by every teacher. This even extends to letters home that are written in symbols if the content needs to be accessible to the students as well as their parents/ carers. The students enjoy being able to recognise individual symbols or read a few words. For example, it is more inclusive for schools to send letters home which have symbols rather than all text letters from which the students are excluded.

RHS

REDBRIDGE HIGH SCHOOL

Sherwoods Lane
Fazakerley
Liverpool
L10 1LW

Tel: 0151 525 5733
Fax: 0151 524 0435

Headteacher: Shelagh Coates B.Ed (Hons) M.B. A. (Ed)

Dear parents

We are going to the pub for lunch for Anthony's 18th birthday. We will need our travel passes and £5 for our lunch.

Thank you.

John

Joanna

Pauline

William

*A letter sent home to parents regarding an outing.*

## Making the transition from primary to secondary school

➤ Primary school pupils have to cope with transition as they face what can be a daunting move on to a bigger secondary school. Heathside School is a primary school in Ipswich for pupils with profound and severe learning difficulties. Teacher Sara Pells uses PCS and Rebus symbols with the children.

> 'Symbols are used to convey information to the pupils throughout their working day. They are used in communication books and communication aids, and we develop simple worksheets and recording sheets for pupils to use. Symbols are used as a prompt to read text from books, by placing symbols under or above written texts in big books or small readers.'

Sara recognises that problems may arise if consistency is not addressed before pupils transfer to secondary school.

> 'We are trying to agree 100 basic symbols as an introductory package for our pupils in special schools. We are also trying to liaise with our senior school on agreed use of subject or activity symbols. We plan to make subject specific sheets of these symbols available.'

## Making the transition from school to adult life

➤ At Redbridge High School the students are actively involved in compiling their record of achievement folders throughout their school career. The use of symbols to annotate work, photos and other items included in their folders has meant that when students take these to interviews they are able to use the symbols as an 'aide memoire' to help them to talk more confidently and more fully about their achievements. The record of achievement is an important way of transferring information from school to post-school placement. Symbols have enabled the students to take a far more active part in this transfer of information than previously. The students' National Record of Achievement documents are also produced using symbols so that the young people can read their own documents - either literally, or by using individual key word symbols as cues helping them to understand what the information is about - it is, after all, THEIR document.

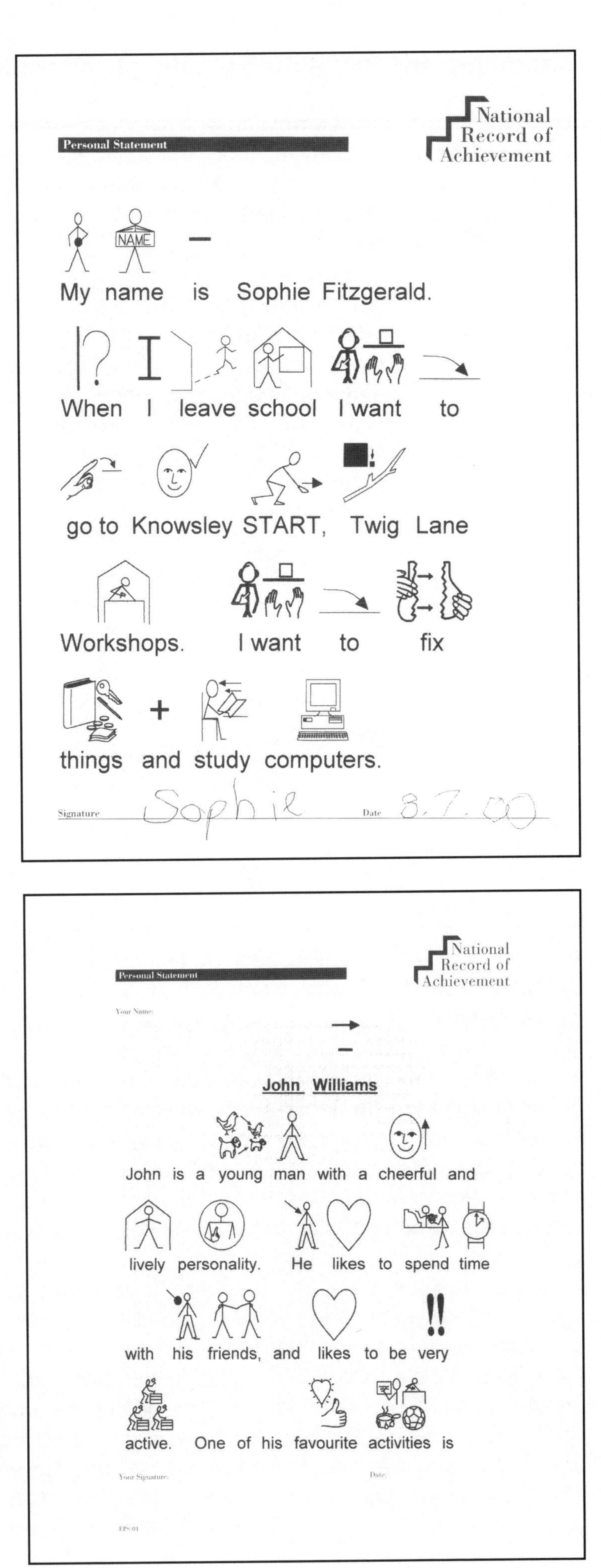

Personal Statement

National Record of Achievement

My name is Sophie Fitzgerald.

When I leave school I want to go to Knowsley START, Twig Lane Workshops. I want to fix things and study computers.

Signature Sophie Date 8.7.00

Personal Statement

National Record of Achievement

Your Name:

John Williams

John is a young man with a cheerful and lively personality. He likes to spend time with his friends, and likes to be very active. One of his favourite activities is

Your Signature: Date:

*Extracts from student's Records of Achievement at Redbridge High School.*

## Choosing and developing sets of symbols

It can be very difficult determining which specific set of symbols is best in any context. Some schools and centres, like Heathside School, have found themselves able to standardise this choice: either from the symbol sets currently available, or by developing a modified set of their own.

➤ Symbols can also be chosen to support progression in understanding. One development described by Char Smith is the use of a symbol-supported calendar for a client recovering from an operation. The calendar covered a month with yes or no symbols stuck on each day to indicate what the user could and could not do. The frequency of symbols appearing on the No side gradually shifted to the Yes side and the user was able to see that she was making progress.

*A calendar used for recording progress over time.*

➤ A team of teachers and speech and language therapists led by Valerie Moffatt at Chailey Heritage School, developed a very comprehensive symbol vocabulary organised in a very efficient structure so that children can quickly find any symbol they want in the system. They worked with Judy van Oosterom and Widgit Software Ltd, using the Rebus symbol set as a base for extending into new areas of vocabulary. For example, there was a great need for symbols to support sex education and personal and social development. The Chailey Communication System which resulted is a comprehensive vocabulary used by many people.

➤ Sometimes it may not be necessary to develop a complete symbol-based system, and all that is needed is a sensitive choice combining appropriate symbols from a number of different types. Nicole Rappell, is a speech and language therapist at Lord Mayor Treloar National Specialist Further Education College, where they spent a long time deciding how to solve what Nicole describes as their 'symbol dilemma.' The college, which has 175 students with physical and learning disabilities aged between 16 and 25 years, decided to aim for a combined list of PCS and Rebus symbols. Nicole explains:

> 'We decided to combine them together as we traditionally use PCS in communication folders. We prioritised according to what we felt was most transparent.'

Nicole is now not so sure that tight control over the symbols used is really the answer.

> 'It is very difficult to co-ordinate with everyone and then upgrade the server. My experience of sitting writing with students is that they have personal preferences for symbols that represent the meaning to them. This is particularly true when you are renaming a little-used symbol to mean something else, for example a tower for Disneyland.'

On the other hand, Nicole knows that the students are often more flexible than we sometimes give them credit for.

> 'I also think the top-down solution of trying to keep the list the same means that individual tutors are put off from exploring and being creative.'

From discussions with speech and language therapists at Lord Mayor Treloar School, Nicole has found that it is not essential to use the same symbols with children as used in the FE College.

> 'In school the students are younger, many more use PCS-based communication folders and are learning key literacy skills. It was felt that if students were going to require support for their literacy work at an FE level, then Rebus symbols could be introduced slowly in their final years. This does seem messy and confusing – but also realistic. I suppose it very much depends on what the symbols are being used for.'

Nicole found that having used an output communication aid makes it easier for students to master an additional program. She suspects the same may be true of symbol set understandings.

➤ Linda Edwards also discussed on the symbol email forum the issue of controlling symbol selection. At St Piers School, she explains, they started to monitor symbol selection because,

> 'The majority of our users were not relying on symbols to express themselves, but benefitted from them as a means of written communication, which the grapheme users already had access to.'

Because of the large number of students involved, each using a variety of symbols for recording similar information, Linda realised that a standardised method should be available making messages accessible to the majority. She considers this a positive step forward;

> 'This could be considered an integrationist rather than inclusionist approach, but it still represented huge progress over previous times, when you either read the word or could not access the information independently. In our school there is now acceptance of, and time given to, the idea of using whichever symbol (or picture, photo, object etc) means most to individual users, when one is discussing communication systems. We have also moved away from being prescriptive for symbol use in general, for good reasons, but there is far less time available for customising this type of material. As a result, the problem of accessing common documents comes back, and we do not want problems with this to undermine people's confidence in the effectiveness of symbols as a literacy medium.'

As Linda goes on to suggest, a mixture of the two approaches for particular purposes may be the most appropriate answer.

➤ Writing on the symbol email forum, Justin Drew from the West Midlands raised issues involving symbol choice. His main point was that schools should use symbols that are appropriate to the individual child. He also sees symbol use as part of a continuum of literacy and communication development, moving from the most concrete to the most abstract.

> 'In literacy this would mean moving from objects to photos to symbols (PCS or Rebus) and then finally to text.'

This does not however suggest that all learners will move through the complete progression. When choosing between Rebus symbols, PCS or photos to use with PECS, Justin recommends some general principles.

> 'If I feel the student will not develop some form of literacy skill I choose PCS; many students do respond to these where they may not to Rebus. If literacy is a realistic goal, and they can follow and put together symbols to make phrases and understand them, then I go for Rebus. Of course, sometimes students may move between PCS and Rebus. The important thing is that the text will always be there for others to read and understand, and that the symbol in use has been taught to and understood by the student. I have found that using PECS really helps students understand and use symbols to communicate. Symbols can also be more easily generalised than a photo, which may contain too much detail for some students.'

## Developing symbol for specific situations

➤ Jo Egerton, from Sunfield School worked with the physiotherapists to develop a range of symbols for different exercises. This helped the children to have a visual image of what they were doing. Following on from the success of this, she developed a set of symbols to support horse-riding. Symbols for the various grooming implements are included, as are those for the correct clothing to be worn. Another set of symbols covers the different parts of the horse and there are further sets for shoeing, stable management, mucking out, tack, and food.

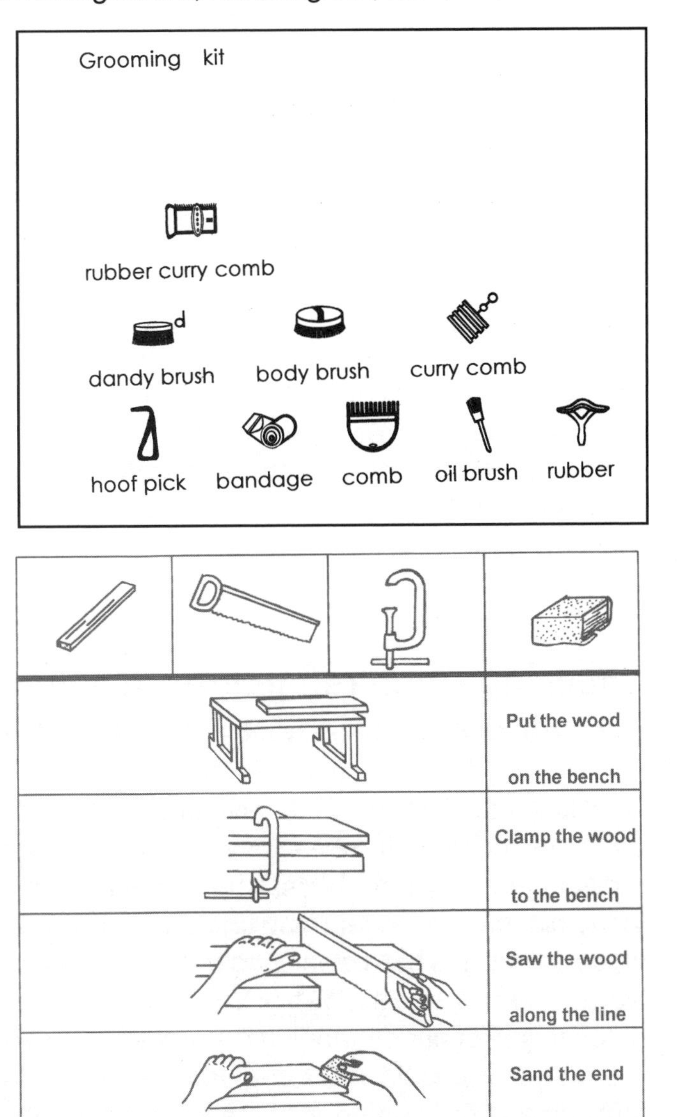


*Symbols developed to support a specialist vocabulary.*

*Symbol task sheets developed by Jackie Stubbs to help a gentleman with autistic difficulties to understand the sequence of events and to know when a certain task was completed.*

These symbols are very specifically designed to relate to the subject area. They are almost illustrations but have a generic quality that makes them usable in wider circumstances.

*Local symbols designed using basic components from the users' normal symbol set.*

➤ In designing these local symbols, Devon Total Communication identified key features for each town or village and added these to the generic 'town' concept. For Totnes the generic element was modified but the source, and thus concept, is still recognisable.

## Checking understanding: making sure that symbol communications are understood

Checking that symbol users have understood what is happening and have made their views known is of central importance when engaging with people who may have difficulties in communication. In the classroom, no learning should be assumed to have taken place unless this has been checked in some way, as is true for all learners of course. At a time of transition, symbols can be a useful mechanism for understanding the wishes of those whose choices are under discussion. Strategies need to be developed within families and care settings to increase understanding of people with learning disabilities. In many cases, resources will need to be personalised to suit local circumstances, but packs may be available that can be used and adapted quickly to suit particular people and settings.

➤ Theresa Latham teaches at South-East Essex College and discovered symbols when reading an article in the *Times Educational Supplement.* She became interested in the extent to which a change of teaching approach using symbols might help pupils develop self-esteem, independence and personal autonomy. Theresa planned some activities using symbols related to the pre-work skills programme at the college. She wanted Simon and Jack, two students with learning difficulties, to take a full and equal part in these activities.

> 'The group had been planning a video activity in my class, in which they were going to introduce their work placements and demonstrate how they dealt with problems which arose. They had been preparing scripts to rehearse to camera.'

At this point Theresa was not using symbol software, but she had been pleased by her students' response to hand-drawn symbols in the past. She decided to prepare symbol-enhanced scripts for the two students.

> 'I was heartened by the way they were able to access the activity on an equal basis with their peers, particularly Simon, who was able to recall the entire content of his speech to camera without prompting, a situation which would raise his self-esteem.'

After the software arrived Theresa checked Simon's understanding of the symbols. Simon dictated his own script but was only able to read back about a quarter of those words without assistance. Jack, on the other hand, could read back the whole script and seemed to need only occasional symbol assistance.

Theresa gave both students an introduction to printed symbols using a worksheet with keywords from their speeches. Both students then read their speeches to the camera again, this time working from a symbolised script. Simon was now much more accurate in his reading, managing more than three-quarters of the words. Jack benefitted from the symbols too and they enabled him to read almost without errors. A week later, Theresa provided Simon with a more fully symbolised script. The first version had omissions where no symbol was immediately available but this had now been amended so that every word had a printed or hand-drawn symbol. He was able to read this script almost as accurately as Jack. Jack, too, made progress with occasional errors: the symbols were particularly useful for helping him to distinguish between 'them' and 'they.'

An interesting evaluation was carried out by Gela Griffiths to check whether symbols really helped users understand text. This is described in Chapter 5.

## Developing strategies for checking understanding

The easiest way of checking understanding is by talking to the communicant. However, they may need resources to help: for example, signing or using individual symbol cards to confirm the key ideas.

*Illustrations give a lot of information to stimulate discussion, whilst symbols can give more precise information for communication.*

➤ *I'll Go First* is a planning and review kit for children with disabilities. It was written by Lucy Kilbride and produced by The Children's Society.The pack is based on the belief that it is vitally important that all children are asked their views when decisions are being made about their future. The pack contains a detailed guide with a wide range of laminated sheets including pictures, text and symbols. The laminated cards can be used with re-usable symbol stickers. The guide contains descriptions of how these resources can be used and strategies that carers can adopt. The cards can be written on with wet wipe or OHP pens and photocopies can be made of the completed cards for each user before wiping the cards clean ready for reuse.

One side of the laminated card has pictures to stimulate discussion and communication.

The reverse of the card has some symbol supported questions or statements. These can be completed by writing or drawing. There are also some symbol stickers which can be added.

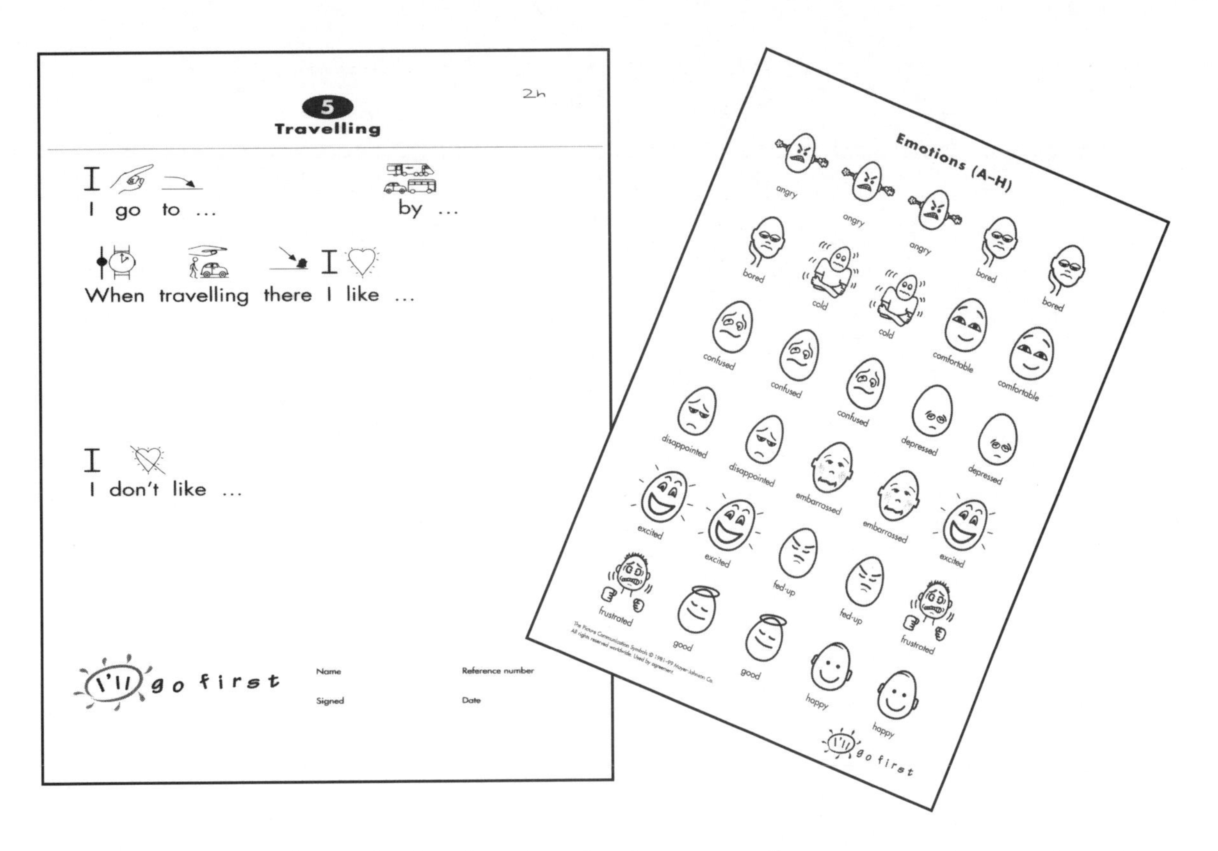


*A laminated card for writing or sticking, with a page of 'feelings' PCS symbols.*

*I'll Go First* was piloted in five local authorities, and the case studies from these pilots are included in the guide. A particular value of the pack is the guidance given on how children's wishes and feelings can be recorded, and the importance of separating the recording of views from dealing with problems. The boards included in the pack are entitled 'This is me', 'More about me', 'My family', 'Going away from home', 'Travelling', 'Activities away from home', 'School', 'People at school', 'I like', 'I don't like', 'Mealtimes', 'Bedtime', 'Going home', 'The next visit', 'My future' and 'Follow-on'.

## Summary

Consistent use of symbols in different settings is of genuine use to symbol users.

Liaison between primary and secondary schools often assists in overcoming problems in certain aspects of the transition between the two phases of schooling for symbol users.

Some users may benefit more from developing their own personalised symbol set or by modifying existing symbols

Using symbols to communicate should be accompanied by checking the understanding of the symbol user.

Symbols enable people with learning difficulties to understand the choices available to them and make their preferences known.

# CHAPTER 4

## COMMUNICATING WITH SYMBOLS

**Symbols can be used in interactive face to face settings as well as in non-interactive environments such as over distances. Symbols have a role to play in many different kinds of communication systems. Communicating electronically with symbols has been made easier with modern technology such as fax and more recently a symbol-based email programme.**

**Although symbols are now accessible as an on-line resource, on-line information providers should be aware of accessibility issues in particular that information could be offered in a symbolised form. In conjunction with this, symbol users need to be offered a small number of choices as opposed to the more confusing screen displays representative of current design trends.**

**Some organisations have developed their own communication systems to meet local needs; symbol choice is often related to individual needs. In other instances, mainstream symbol programmes such as PECS may be more appropriate offering better understanding to users in a variety of settings and with various needs.**

### Why communicate with others?

It is the right of everyone to be able to communicate with others, and this was made clear in the Communication Bill of Rights produced by the American Speech and Hearing Association in 1992. Many of the points in that document have relevance to the use of symbols:

#### A Communication Bill of Rights

All persons, regardless of the extent or severity of their disabilities, have a basic human right to affect, through communication, the conditions of their own existence. Beyond the general right, a number of specific communication rights should be ensured in all daily interactions involving persons who have severe disabilities. These basic communication rights are as follows:

1) The right to request desired objects, actions, events and persons and to express personal preferences or feelings.

2) The right to be offered choices and alternatives.

3) The right to reject or refuse undesired objects, events or actions including the right to decline or request all proffered choices.

4) The right to request, and be given, attention from and interaction with another person.

5) The right to request feedback or information about a state, an object, a person or an event of interest.

6) The right to active treatment and intervention efforts to enable people with severe disabilities to communicate messages in whatever modes and as effectively and efficiently as their specific abilities will allow.

7) The right to have communicative acts acknowledged and responded to, even when the intent of these acts cannot be fulfilled by the responder.

8) The right to have access at all times to any needed augmentative and alternative communication devices and other assistive devices, and to have those devices in good working order.

9) The right to environmental contexts, interactions and opportunities that expect and encourage persons with disabilities to participate as full communicative partners with other people, including peers.

10) The right to be informed about people, things and events in ones immediate environment.

11) The right to be communicated with in a manner that recognises and acknowledges the inherent dignity of the person being addressed including the right to be part of communication exchanges about individuals that are conducted in his or her presence.

12) The right to be communicated with in ways that are meaningful, understandable and culturally and linguistically appropriate.

(The National Joint Committee for the Communication Needs of Persons with Severe Disabilities, 1992, ASHA)

There are two quite different styles of informal communication. Immediate, often face to face, interaction takes place when the partners are able to communicate using several modes together. This is the basis of the total communication approach, used most notably in Devon and Somerset. Symbols are used along with gesture and speech to provide a multi-model communication. Because of the interactive nature of direct communication, symbols can represent just key ideas, and do not need to involve complete language or grammar.

Communication at a distance, where the communicants are not able to interact immediately, requires a different style of symbol use which is comparably new. However on-line and fax communication provide new possibilities for people to exchange ideas and information.

## 1 Communicating Face to Face

➤ Marc Hooker works with symbol users in a residential home for adults with learning difficulties where he manages a team of staff/carers. The team felt the emotional needs of their clients were not being addressed by the use of symbols for basic 'needs' such as 'drink', 'toilet' and 'bed'. One of the clients with communication difficulties expressed himself through aggressive behaviour, and the team thought he might benefit from a system which would allow him to express his emotions. The symbols were made on a laminated communication board; initially the only emotion represented on the board was 'sorry'.

The staff decided to make a second board for the client enabling him to express his emotional state. Six emotions were selected; 'sad', 'happy', 'angry', 'tired', 'funny' and 'confused'. The aim was to cover a range of emotions including those that were positive, negative and neutral. The symbols were introduced as individual laminated cards. Marc explains the next step:

> 'A member of staff working with the client discussed each emotion: saying the word, holding up the symbol and making the appropriate facial expression. Sessions lasted for ten minutes in a room where the client was comfortable. The client was encouraged to make the appropriate facial expression when a symbol was selected by the staff member and then the client was invited to select one for the staff member to mime.'

The decision was made to start with positive emotions, and to introduce 'angry' and 'sad' at a later stage.

After a few months the client used the emotion board to initiate conversation with staff. Sometimes he would indicate he was tired when he returned from the day centre, so would go to bed earlier than usual. The client often became aggressive, shouting and throwing objects, the next plan was to help him express the anxieties which provoked this state of mind.

The emotion board was also used to help the client understand that sometimes carers feel sad or angry, or may need time before they are willing to forgive behaviour that has taken place, as Marc explains;

> 'When the client appeared comfortable and able to acknowledge that his aggression towards others caused them to feel sad, staff felt the next stage was to help the client to understand that, after an incident, the other person - resident or staff member - may need time away from him.'

There was therefore a delay before the customary handshake of reconciliation took place, this was explained by use of both a clock symbol and the 'sad' emotion.

Since the board was developed, several years ago, the client has continued to use it and carry it about with him. Marc recognises that it has not been a total success however:

> 'Use of the board remains erratic. On some occasions he will use it, usually following a request from a staff member that he do so. The time-out concept was found difficult to put into practice, but the main success has been the way in which the board has helped him to communicate his emotional state.'

Staff have put the 'angry' symbol on a cushion, so it can be thrown or punched when anger is the dominant emotion; a safe and effective way of managing this feeling.

### Symbols promoting interaction

The developments of Total Communication approaches, as well as the rapid development of the American symbol system, Picture Exchange Communication System (PECS), indicate a considerable interest in the area of supporting and encouraging interaction and communication between symbol users and the wider community.

➤ Justin Drew is a specialist speech and language therapist working at Glebefields Health Centre in the West Midlands. He uses PECS and other approaches with his clients in both special and mainstream schools, in other settings and to support therapy in hospitals. He also uses Aided Language Display (ALD) symbol sheets for specific activities. Among the uses developed by Justin are visual timetables, communication books, worksheets for teaching grammar and vocabulary as well as shopping lists. Communication aids, both high and low tech, are also used, but it is PECS which forms the integral part of his work.

PECS offers a clearly structured approach to teaching functional communication skills to young children, older pupils and adults with autism and other communication difficulties. PECS was developed twelve years ago in the USA, and has attracted a lot of attention because it concentrates on users initiating communication.

*PCS symbols put into a grid to create resources for Picture Exchange Communication.*

| I want | I see | I hear | sock | book | playdough | biscuit |
|---|---|---|---|---|---|---|
| ball | car | bricks | sweets | crisps | puzzle | apple |
| banana | animals | pop | orange juice | milk | water | shoe |
| bubbles | game | pencil | hoops | toast | chocolate | toys |
| shaker | walkman | computer | lego | toilet | finish | stop |

The PECS focuses on teaching people with learning disabilities to request items and/or activities that can be reinforcing and highly motivating for them. Through the aid of symbols and pictures children and adults can learn to request items as well as learn to initiate communication. By placing pictures or symbols in a communicative partner's hand and later producing sentences using two or three symbols to express their needs, they become successful and communication is achieved. Communication books containing a sentence strip can be developed and personalised to include preferred activities, foods, objects as well as attributes describing items by colour, size, shape and number. As PECS is taught it develops as a mechanism to teach new skills, for example, to comment on what is seen, heard or to describe an item or experience. Speech, or attempts at speech, usually follow prompted by visual stimulus of pictures and symbols.

*A story prompt for Goldilocks and the Three Bears. The symbols on this comunication page can be used to re-tell a story, or to join in a story telling activity.*

| | | | |
|---|---|---|---|
| Goldilocks | cottage | porridge | hot |
| cold | chair | broken | bed |
| hard | soft | big | little |
| bear | crying | angry | turn the page |

**Making communication accessible to people with autism**

People with autism find communication a challenge. The nature of much of our communication means that people with autism are inherently disadvantaged. Much of what we communicate is in tone of voice, gestures, body language and facial expression. Take away the ability to understand these, and you are only able to take the literal meaning of what is said to you - in a society that often does not say what it means or mean what it says, but uses complex systems of idioms, metaphors or similes. Trying to understand communication is like trying to break a code. It is very difficult, very misleading and incredibly frustrating.

This is where symbols can help. A symbol is concrete, visual and permanent. The TEACCH system, developed in North Carolina, considers autism a culture and has identified that people with autism find visual, permanent communication systems much more easy to understand than aural, temporary ones. Routine and structure, with learned systems of working, can reduce the anxiety often experienced by people with autism and enable them to increase their independence, improve their understanding and reduce behavioural difficulties they experience.

➤ Symbols are used extensively when working with people with autism. Wendy Wardle and her colleagues at Ysgol y Graig use PCS and Rebus pictures/symbols in the classroom and in residential areas. Communication books have also been developed. At Redbridge High School the two TEACCH classes use symbols to produce timetables so that the children can see what is going to happen that day. In Mandy's class, as activities are finished, the symbols are put away, thus clearly showing what is going to happen next. Knowing when activities are finished is difficult for people with autism and the putting away of the symbol demonstrates this in a more concrete way.

Photos and symbols are also used as cues whilst students are carrying out activities, so one of Mandy's students, Sophie, carries a photo of the class register with her when she takes it to the office, reminding her where she is going and why. Without the symbol, Sophie used to forget where she was going and what she was doing and many a search party was sent around the school to track her down! Symbols used in these ways have had a significant impact on the students' quality of life, increasing independence skills and reducing frustration.

Many parents have been so impressed with the difference symbols have made that they have asked to have sets at home to improve consistency and to help communication and behaviour. Some parents have even bought symbol software to use on their own PCs to make communication books, symbols and resources to use at home.

**Symbols supporting communication**

➤ Several areas of the UK, notably Oldham, Somerset and South Devon, have developed their own communication approaches. The examples from below show just some of the ways in which this is working. There are many other centres taking a Total Communication approach, doing similar work. In Dorset, Sheryn Biggs uses Total Communication at the residential further education college where she works. Her students are all aged over seventeen and have a variety of special educational needs. As Sheryn explains,

> 'The majority of our learners have no, or few literacy skills. Symbols are used for communication to allow them access to their own work, as a source of information and to increase their independence – an important issue as these are young adults.'

➤ Julie Marples also uses Somerset Total Communication, in mainstream schools across Somerset.

> 'I work with children with physical disabilities who have little or no speech, their peer group, families and school staff (including pre-school). All of the children with disabilities use signs and/or symbols to communicate. The symbols are used in a talking book format and to record or differentiate school work. The type of symbol we use depends on the child's age and understanding, so it's really useful for us to have different symbols sets to use all on one software program.

> Symbols are also starting to be used in a more general sense in the mainstream school where we support children with physical disabilities, this is partly due to increased awareness through training and partly due to having easy access to WWS2000. Teachers have requested sets of symbols for timetable activities, choosing time and days of the week to use with all their class. An assistant who recently started using symbols with children in a year 1 class said "This is the first time that some of the children have been able to read a sentence by themselves".'

Needless to say, Julie hopes that this development will continue in the future.

➤ The Devon Total Communication Partnership has developed a similar range of resources. A recent area of work has involved making care plans and care planning process more accessible. As the first section of this is complete, the Partnership is now looking at ways to ensure the process is interactive and the person concerned is actively involved.

## 2 Communicating at a Distance

### Widening horizons

➤ When Meldreth Manor School won the special schools section of the Microsoft Road Ahead award for their website, they also introduced a great many people to the existence of symbols. The website (http://www.meldrethmanor.com) begins with a choice of six symbols and is designed to link with the more elaborate intranet which operates within the school. Meldreth Manor is a symbol-using school, so it is logical that their website uses symbols.

Other schools and centres have been communicating electronically with symbols, usually by facsimile. The most recent version of Writing with Symbols 2000 makes it possible for symbol users to send and receive email without textual menus being involved, and this is likely to lead to a large increase in this activity.

### Sending symbol messages by FAX

➤ Elleray Park Community Learning Disability (CLD) School in Wallasey have been faxing symbol messages for several years now, and the primary-aged pupils at this school are familiar with the activity. The school uses symbols for emergent literacy and for sequencing. They have even recycled old Breakthrough to Literacy holders, familiar to many teachers, for displaying symbol sentences. Writing with Symbols is used to make diaries for children with autism, and to print the symbol messages which are faxed to other schools. The symbols themselves are sometimes used in what the school describes as a 'low-tech' colour and code system for some of the children.

The most developed electronic method of communication at Elleray Park is the facsimile machine, of which the school has three. These were obtained via the BT Faxbuddies project, a good example of how getting involved in projects can lead to funding and support by big organisations/businesses. As there are three fax machines, different classes are able to fax each other. Most of these faxes use the school symbol bank, a collection of symbols specific to the students, developed by the language co-ordinator who is also a speech and language therapist.

Dear friends

I've just had a holiday in Butlins with
my Mummy and Daddy.
We had great fun,

love

Paul

Dear friends,

I was 7 on Saturday. L had a party. My friends
came. A magician made puppets out of balloons,

love Amanda.

*Faxes from staff and pupils at Ellary Park school. Examples from Making Communication Special*

The school sees the fax as a vital part of their effort to help pupils understand more about communication. They feel it helps to develop a sense of place in students, and it helps them to progress from interpreting symbols to growing a sense of self. The type of fax used can be an issue, and for most schools a digital memory is a useful facility. In combination with this, photo or symbol buttons can be created so the pupils can press these to fax a particular person. Fax is now also possible via the Internet, so it may not always be necessary for a classroom to be equipped with a fax machine in order to send and receive faxes.

**Email communication**

➤ Elleray Park have also started using emails: their first one was about Everton Football Club and sent to Widgit Software. It was sent in text format then pasted into the Writing with Symbols programme. The school is now looking forward to using a full email facility, Inter_Comm devised by Widgit Software.

Inter_Comm is designed so that symbol users can access all aspects of emailing with the minimum of support. All of the functions, such as sending and downloading emails, are available through icons, and the address book entries are represented by photographs or symbols.

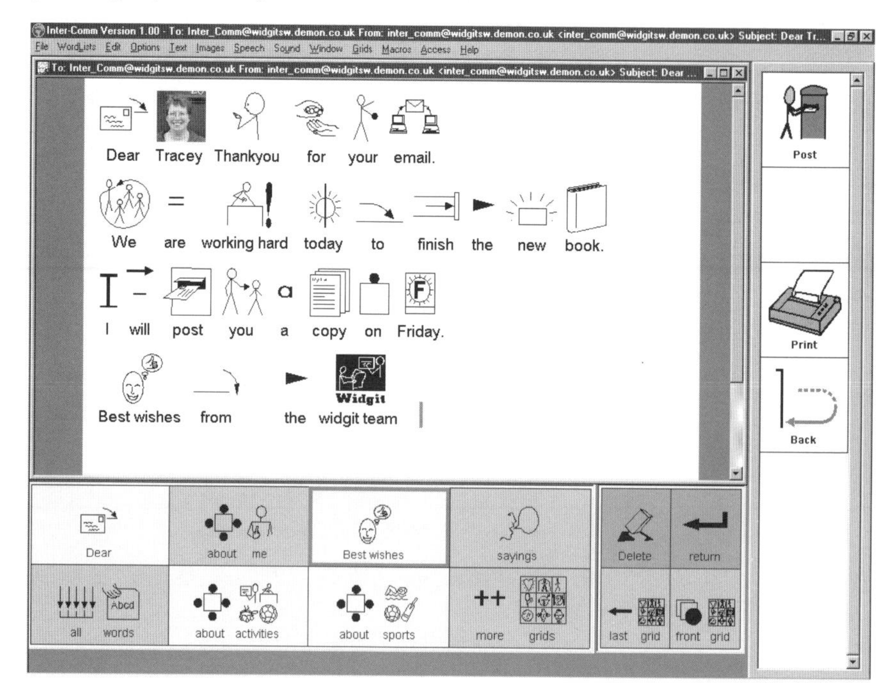


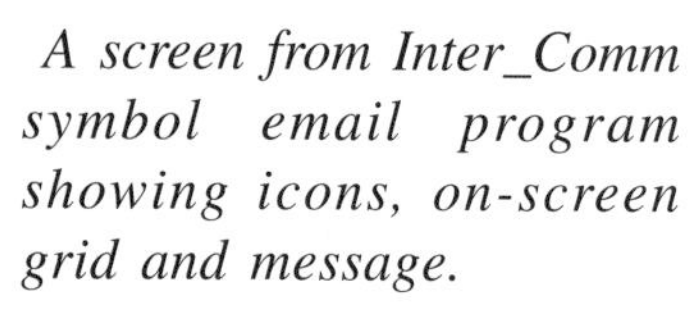

*A screen from Inter_Comm symbol email program showing icons, on-screen grid and message.*

➤ Little Heath School in Romford, Essex are experienced symbol and email users. By symbols they mean a collection of symbols, clipart and digitised images all used for communication purposes. The school uses online school partnering services like Netlinks to find places to communicate with, using the postal services for interesting items that cannot be sent digitally. All pupils have their own email address and the school hosts a wide range of Internet and email projects with schools and individuals throughout the world.

One of the projects Little Heath is involved with is Spike the travelling teddy bear. This project is designed to help young people with special educational needs to both develop their learning and communication skills and find out about people in other parts of the world. Spike's travels will be recorded through photographs and diary entries, pupils at the school will be able to keep in touch with him through email and the internet. In this way, the students become 'virtual visitors to another country and develop important life skills in literacy, numeracy and information technology.

*Spike the travelling bear*

Pupils use email internally to discuss issues with each other and their teachers. This is a good example of how email does not always have to be a means for contacting someone on the other side of the world. In many cases it is appropriate, but also sometimes more effective, to use it to communicate with people who children are likely to also meet face-to-face.

**Symbols on the Web**

➤ Meldreth Manor School is not alone in developing a symbolised website, although the Meldreth site is certainly one of the most extensive and innovative sites around. Mandeville School, a school for pupils with severe learning difficulties in Ealing, has developed a symbol website too. It has been designed particularly with the needs of the school's students in mind.

*The first page of the pupil's area on the Meldreth Manor School web site.*

The Meldreth Manor School site http://www.meldrethmanor.com has an area which can be accessed by switch users. The icones at the top corners of the pages are always in the same place making navigation possible. The symbol icons link to symbol pages for the students to follow,

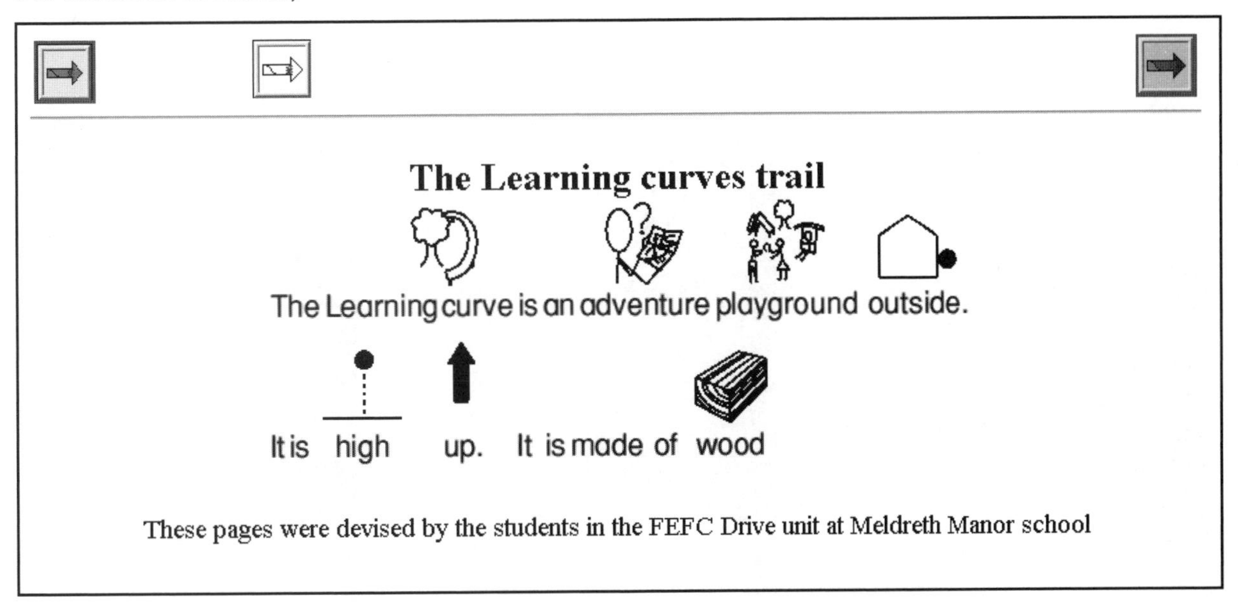


*A web page designed by students from Meldreth Manor School.*

An awareness of audience is crucial for website design particularly when using symbols. Some sites are aimed at parents so that they know what is happening at a school, whereas others are aimed at prospective parents and function mostly as a multimedia advertisement. Numerous other sites are aimed at being a resource for pupils; while others are resource centres for teachers and may have little to offer students or parents. Of course, there is nothing to stop a site trying to do more than one of these: but each will require a separate interface and separate upkeep, so this is no small task.

It is important, of course, that anyone putting information on the Web should ensure it is accessible to all. Web accessibility standards are being developed internationally (http://www.w3.org/WAI/) but it is also possible for a school or service to check that its own site is essentially accessible by sending the address to the Bobby service at http://www.cast.org/bobby/. This will check that all seems well, and if it is, the site can carry the Bobby mark of approval.

➤ Other projects look at the area of symbols on the Web, including the IRALD Project (Information Resources for Adults with Learning Disabilities) funded by Leicestershire Health which provides online health information. The Glebe House Project in Loughborough carried out much of the work on this project, combining the skills and knowledge of an IT consultant and speech and language therapist. The project began by collating views of clients using a carefully-designed questionnaire. Symbols and photographs were used to help with understanding and the results showed that although people with learning disabilities were interested in health care issues, they usually relied on their carers to make appointments for them. The most popular topics included health, such as sport, leisure, entertainment and education.

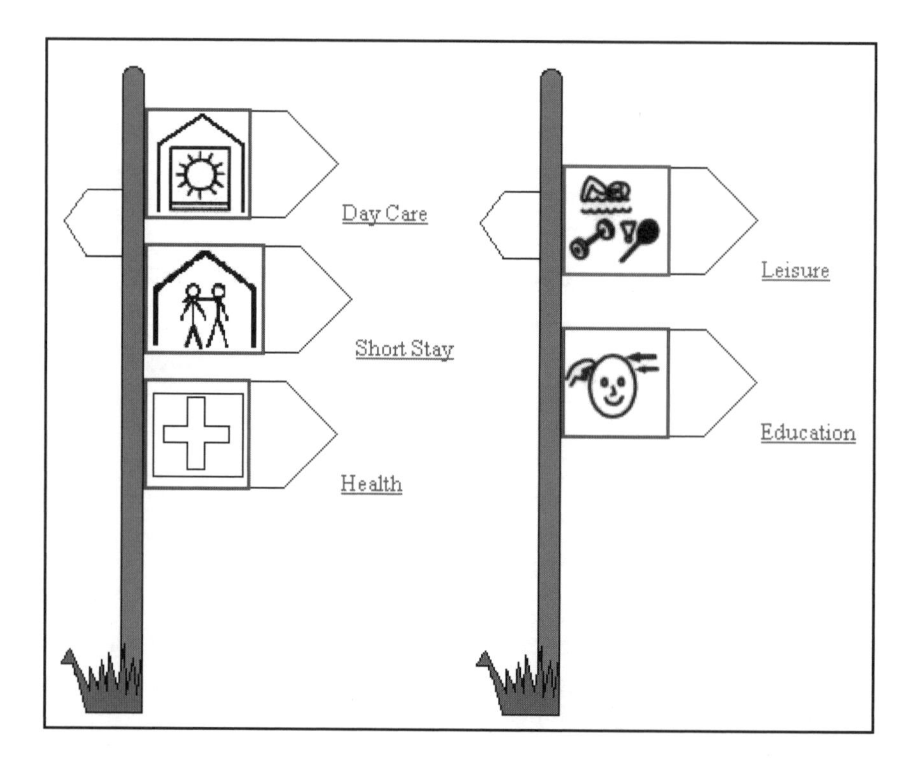


*The signposted home page of the IRALD website.*

IRALD was set up as a research project to explore the ways in which adults with learning disabilities can access information via the internet. The internet offers the opportunity to create individual web pages. This mode of presenting information is ideal for people with learning disabilities as a combination of photos, symbols, drawings and words can be used.

An assessment was made as to how effective at using a computer each client/user attending the centre was. Particular attention was given to visual recognition, motor skills, cognitive ability and sequencing skills. This was achieved through a specially-designed online task which used both photographs of staff and clients. Fourteen of the twenty-two clients assessed were found to have sufficient ability, and they formed the core group for the project. The project found that, when designing accessible web pages, it was essential to limit the number of visual items on a page. Written information should be simple and linked to images, the interface should be consistent and unambiguous. So far, the project has produced online information of this kind for day care, respite care, health, leisure and education.

The day care environment helps clients make choices about their daily activities using a pictorial timetables. Information about other day care centres also helps to raise an awareness of possibilities of choices for viewers. The 'short stay' area on the site is a map with symbol buttons to display pictures of rooms which parents and clients can view before going to the centre. It can also be a reassurance, or a reminder for clients who have been there before. The leisure information gives information about a local country park, with the education area describing the further education college. The health area has information issues such as healthy eating, glaucoma and may add a section developed on breast care; however, this may not be appropriate as an online resource.

Clients have responded very well to this online information. Staff have found the resource useful as a teaching aid, and as preparation before a visit. They also discovered that removing the keyboard from view made the activity more comfortable and television-like, and that more clients could make use of a mouse or mouse-alternative than they had initially expected. Information regarding this project can be found at http://www.u-net.com/irald/

➤ The Toby Homes Site has an area of symbol with information for symbol readers to access. The menu icons are symbols to help navigation, and these pages have information about their homes, and the activities that go on there. The Anthony Toby Homes Trust was founded in 1975 by a group of professionals and interested people to support people with learning disabilities and their families in the Bracknell and Wokingham area.

The address for these pages is http://www.tobyhomes.freeserve.co.uk/ There are many pages of symbol information which are easily navigated using icons.

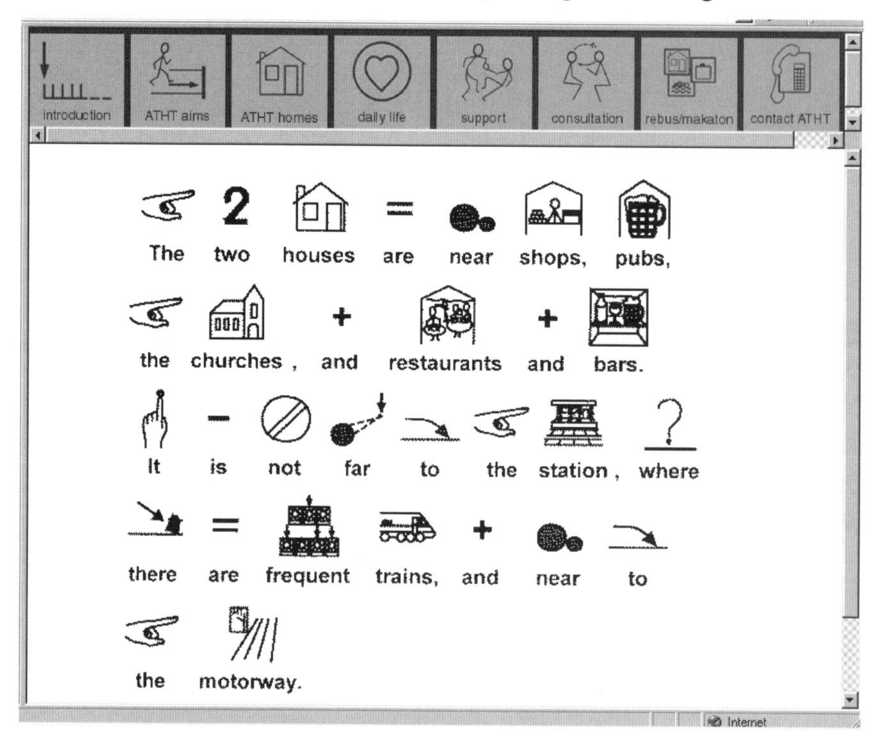


*A page from the Toby Homes website. These pages are designed for symbol readers. Navigation is through icons.*

## Summary

Symbol choice may best be related to individual needs rather than to specific systems.

Communication systems have been developed locally to meet local needs.

Recent developments in technology now provide for and encourage the wide spread use of symbol communication.

Symbols users are able to access on-line resources if it is available in symbol form.

On-line information providers need to be aware of accesibility issues.

Symbol users respond better to a small number of choices when searching on-line rather than complicated screen displays.

Symbols have a role to play in numerous communication systems.

Mainstream symbol systems may have much to offer users in a variety of settings and with varied needs.

# CHAPTER 5

## SYMBOLS FOR ACCESSING INFORMATION

**Accessibility of information can be promoted through the use of symbols. Official information can take many forms, from providing access to leisure activities to ensuring safety information is understood. Often this information has a direct bearing on symbol user's lives and well-being. When presented in symbol format, official information can provide access to complex information for symbol users.**

**Symbols are also used to support people in their daily lives and preparing themselves for new challenges.**

**Where the information is informal users can make their own decisions about symbol choice, but in more formal information, where the readership is wide, it is helpful to have guidelines to aid consistency and readability.**

➤ Redbridge High School has integrated the use of symbols into all areas of the curriculum, and found that a generation of increasingly symbol-literate learners were emerging who expected symbols to be available to them as a matter of course. It also became apparent that there were other areas that needed to incorporate the use of symbols. Gela Griffiths, the careers co-ordinator at the school, found the careers service that worked with their students, Career Decisions, produced a transitional action plan for her students as they prepared to leave school at nineteen.

The careers advisor, John, spent a lot of time with the young people getting to know them and working with them to produce action plans. These were then typed - without the support of symbols - making an otherwise valuable document inaccessible to the students who needed it. To improve ownership of the documents, Gela approached the Careers Service and asked if they would support the school in developing a pilot project.

Gela worked with John and the careers service special needs manager, Jan, to run a pilot study producing action plans with symbols. But how would they know whether the symbols had actually helped the student to understand what was written? They decided to give the students a text-only version of the action plan and count how many words they could read, and then give them the symbol version and check again how many words were read. The students were allowed to make mistakes and any mistakes were not corrected when reading the text-only version so that they did not have a head start when reading the symbol version.

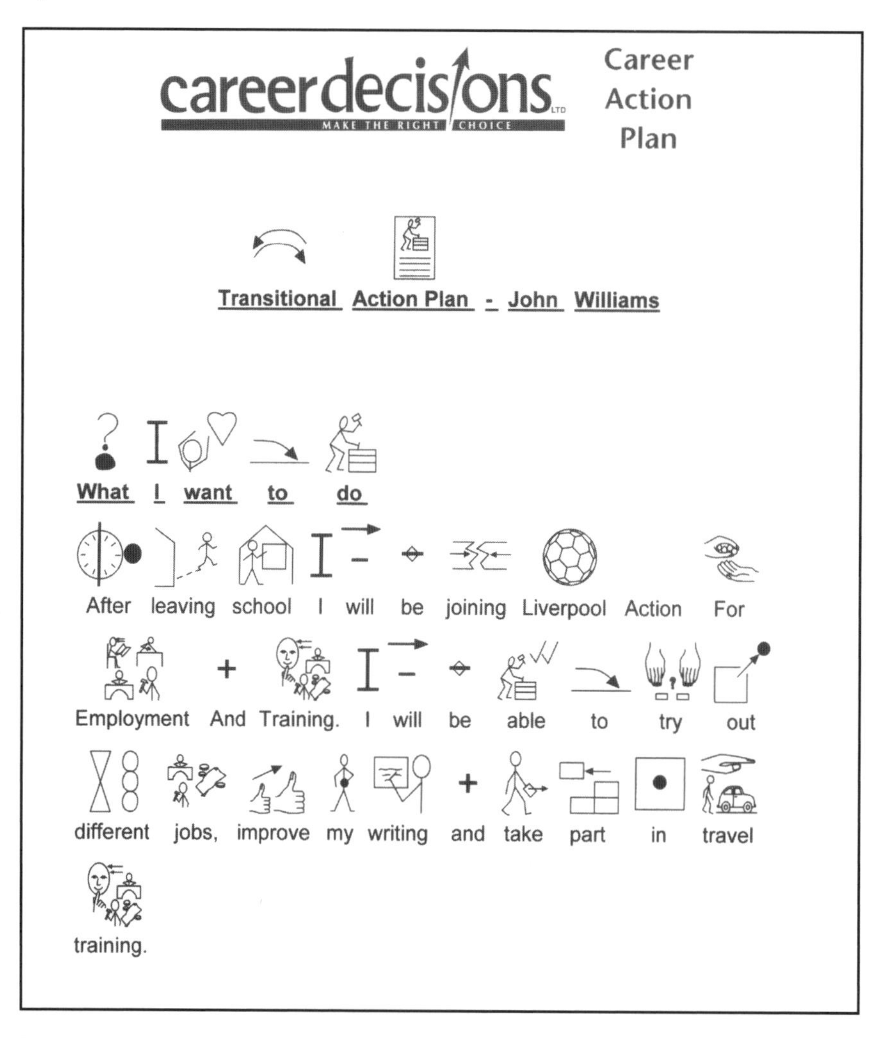

careerdecisions LTD
MAKE THE RIGHT CHOICE

Career Action Plan

Transitional Action Plan - John Williams

What I want to do

After leaving school I will be joining Liverpool Action For Employment And Training. I will be able to try out different jobs, improve my writing and take part in travel training.

The main lessons learned were that careful choice of language could improve the readability of a phrase, so that 'attend college' was more easily read as 'go to college.' This was a training issue for the careers service and a support issue for the school working with the careers service showing the need to share experience and skills. Careful choice of symbols was also an important point, as sometimes the first symbol that appeared on screen was not the most appropriate symbol for a particular word. For example work can be identified as desk work or more physical/practical work and there are symbols for both.

If one symbol tends to be used in preference to another within the school, it makes sense to use this in the Action Plan as it is more likely to be recognised. This process will be refined and improved each time it is completed with a group of students. Gela and the staff team are now looking at how students with autism, or profound and multiple learning difficulties, can be helped to achieve a meaningful understanding of their action plans.

The success of the pilot study also lead to using symbols in many other areas of the school's careers education programme. The next area to be developed was in providing accessible careers information, especially about possible post-school placements. The students have also been involved in the production of photo and symbol careers information booklets about the options available when they leave school. These are readily available to students and have a key word symbol on one page, with a photo and a short sentence accompanied by symbols on the opposite page.

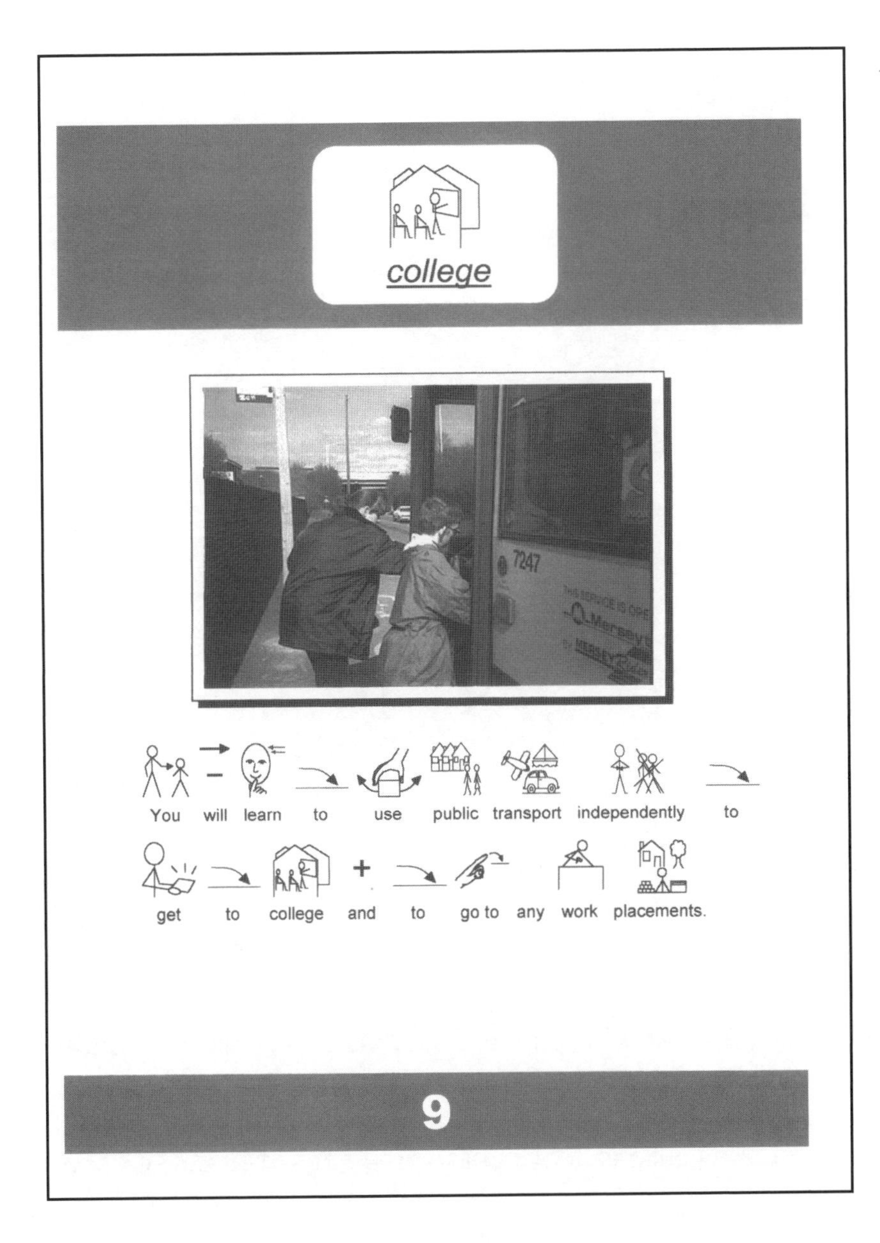


*A page from a Careers Information Book. The high quality of presentation improves the status of the material.*

Each page gives the reader simple information about post-school placements which can be taken home to discuss with parents. The students enjoy being able to look at them frequently, using them at break-times and discussing them with their friends who are also leaving school. As students have access to symbols from an earlier age, we can expect to see an increasingly symbol-literate school population, these young people will have access to different services when leaving school.

➤ In Surrey, a 'Choices and Decisions' booklet was produced in a symbolised form with support from the Guildford and Godalming Education & Business Partnership. The booklet deals with issues arising at college, day services and in work experience. It is designed to help students who are visiting centres to choose where they will attend in future. The booklet also helps students to determine which workshops to attend during their visit. Gill Lloyd also devised much of the work used in the Steps Portfolio, a set of resources to help pupils through the important steps of making decisions about their future lives.

*A student's completed questionnaire in the book, as well as finding out about different options. This page was from a section entitled: Think about yourself. What can you do and what do you like doing?*

➤ Lufton Manor and Dilston are both part of the National Further Education College run by MENCAP and offer further education and training for people with learning disabilities. Like all educational institutions, they publish brochures to attract students.

Symbols are used in the brochures to help make the information as accessible as possible. Each page displays three mediums of printed communication. Photographs show various aspects of college life followed by a description in text, with a summary of symbols. Using symbols in the brochures provides a supportive role that is effective in making the information accessible to a wide audience.

# Where will I live?

If you do a day course, you will live at home. If you live at the college, you will have a room in a cottage, a flat, or in the main building with other students.

*An extract from a brochure about Lufton Manor communicating in three mediums; text, photographs and symbols.*

➤ The Pathway Employment Service in Bristol have produced a Health and Safety guide using 'Easy English' alongside symbols. Topics covered include the use of protective equipment, reporting accidents and liability insurance.

*An information sheet explaining employment rights, and a health and safety notice giving advice.*

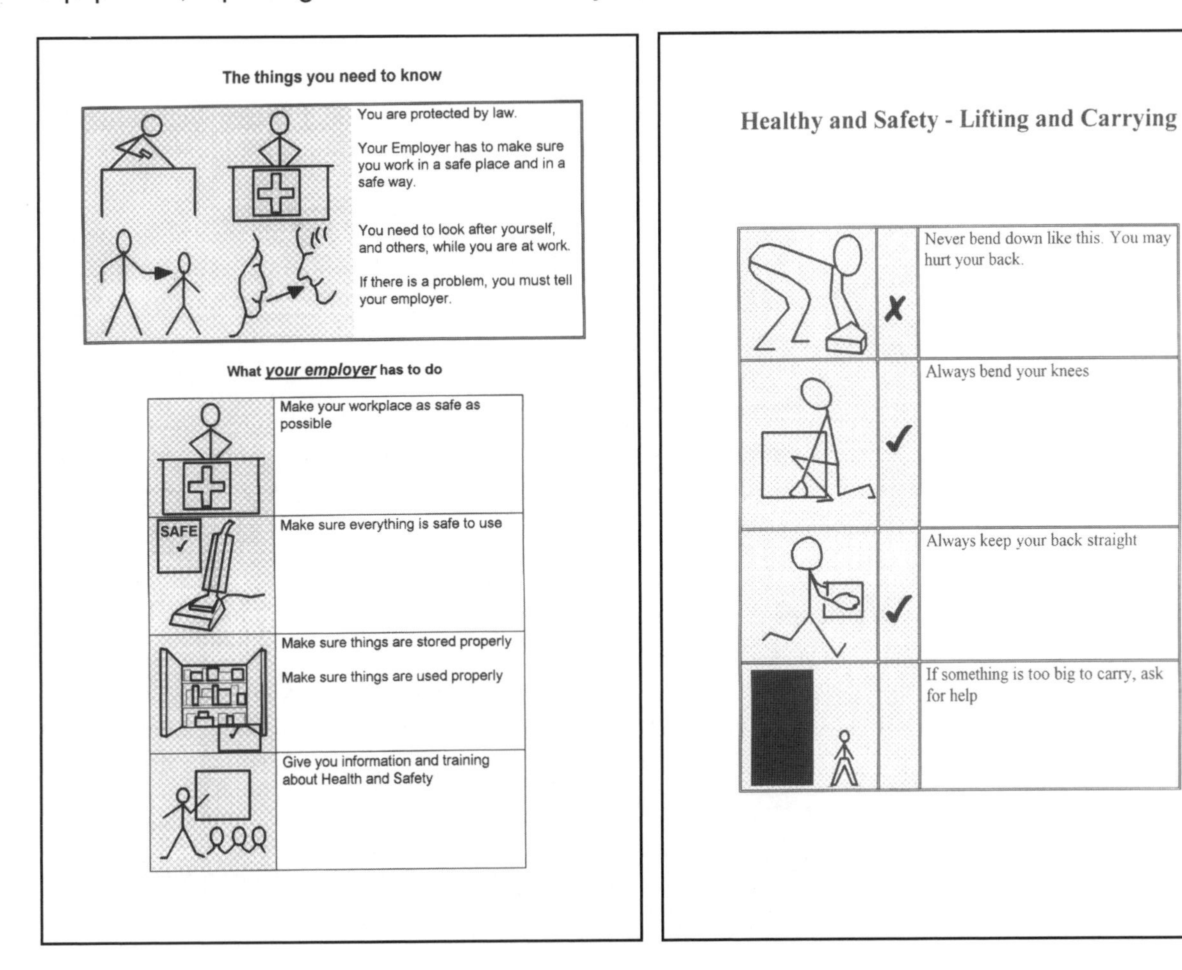

**The things you need to know**

You are protected by law.

Your Employer has to make sure you work in a safe place and in a safe way.

You need to look after yourself, and others, while you are at work.

If there is a problem, you must tell your employer.

**What *your employer* has to do**

Make your workplace as safe as possible

SAFE ✓ — Make sure everything is safe to use

Make sure things are stored properly

Make sure things are used properly

Give you information and training about Health and Safety

**Healthy and Safety - Lifting and Carrying**

| | | |
|---|---|---|
| | ✗ | Never bend down like this. You may hurt your back. |
| | ✓ | Always bend your knees |
| | ✓ | Always keep your back straight |
| | | If something is too big to carry, ask for help |

Another section looks at the role of employer and employee in a cleaning co-operative. There is also a section on types of fire extinguishers, which is in colour to indicate the coding used for different types. A linked document, also produced by the Pathway Employment Service, is a symbolised employment contract listing the rights and responsibilities of both workers and management.

➤ Claire Richards works for the day care service in Surrey that supports older adults with learning disabilities. Many of her clients have been resettled from long-stay institutions. Symbols are used by this group in a variety of ways, for example, in letters, minutes, plans and timetables. The day centre also uses symbols for Christmas cards, choice cards, the centre's day board and notices about fire drill. Key fobs, door signs and communication books have also been produced as well as publicity material, workshop fliers, reviews, Bingo and other games, recipes, newsletters and labels eg, on kitchen cupboards. Maps have been made more accessible with symbols, as have the visitors' guide and the IT facilities at the centre.

The Surrey Symbols Working Group, to which Claire belongs, have bid for funding to offer symbolising support to others outside the day care service, including care managers, users, carers, libraries and even places of interest like McDonalds. As part of a schools awareness campaign, symbols have also been used on a CD cover, with murals and art work and in diary entries.

The group has produced some good practice guidelines on using symbols. In their introduction they explain

> "People have a fundamental right to information about things that affect their life. Information is rarely designed in a way that people with learning disabilities easily read and understand. ....
>
> When we say accessible we mean that people can understand the information without support, accessing it themselves instead of relying on someone else to explain it."

They go on to say

> "Symbols have been proved as an effective way of making information much more accessible, though even when symbols are used many people still need support to access information."

Similar activities occur in other counties such as in Wiltshire at the Marlborough day service. Here, a range of different symbols are used to make users' meetings minutes accessible, and to help users understand a wide range of public information. Menus and daily activities at the centre are also symbolised.

➤ Ann Hyde is a MENCAP development worker who is interested in the use of symbols and has a personal copy of the software Writing with Symbols. She works with adults living at home, in residential homes or at day centres. All the adults she works with have learning difficulties. She makes brochures to help users make choices for educational and leisure activities and to express their ideas from forums that have helped them put forward their opinions. Symbols are also used to write personal and business letters, as well as individual timetables. In future, Ann plans to extend these uses so greater access can be given to review meetings and better support provided for those with the greatest need. She hopes to persuade people working in social services and other areas to improve the quality of their communication they have with users. Ann hopes to see symbol use promoting independence for individuals and providing the opportunity for increased communication to other parts of the UK and abroad. One of her personal interests is how symbols can help a wider group of young people especially those who find spelling difficult.

➤ Julie Russ works in an Ability Housing Association home for adults with learning disabilities. She uses symbol software to produce the minutes of residents' meetings so that the residents are able to read them. Currently a mixture of symbols is used for staff rotas and client diaries. In future, Julie and her colleagues would like to extend the use of symbols to encourage clients to use them more fully in their diaries.

➤ Similarly, Real Voice Media in Bristol have adopted the use of symbols to produce community care plans, magazines, constitutions, charters, child protection documentation, Minutes, evaluations and letters, which have proved popular in all areas of the community.

➤ Jane Young teaches at the Isle of Wight College. Her further education students with learning disabilities use symbols in a variety of ways. The college produces a printed brochure for adults with learning disabilities which uses symbols to help prospective students choose the courses they wish to follow. Symbols are also used for assessments and for information signs around the college. Refectory menus are symbolised as are a variety of course brochures, handouts and disability statements. Within classrooms symbols are used where possible in worksheets, recipes, shopping lists, letters and displays.

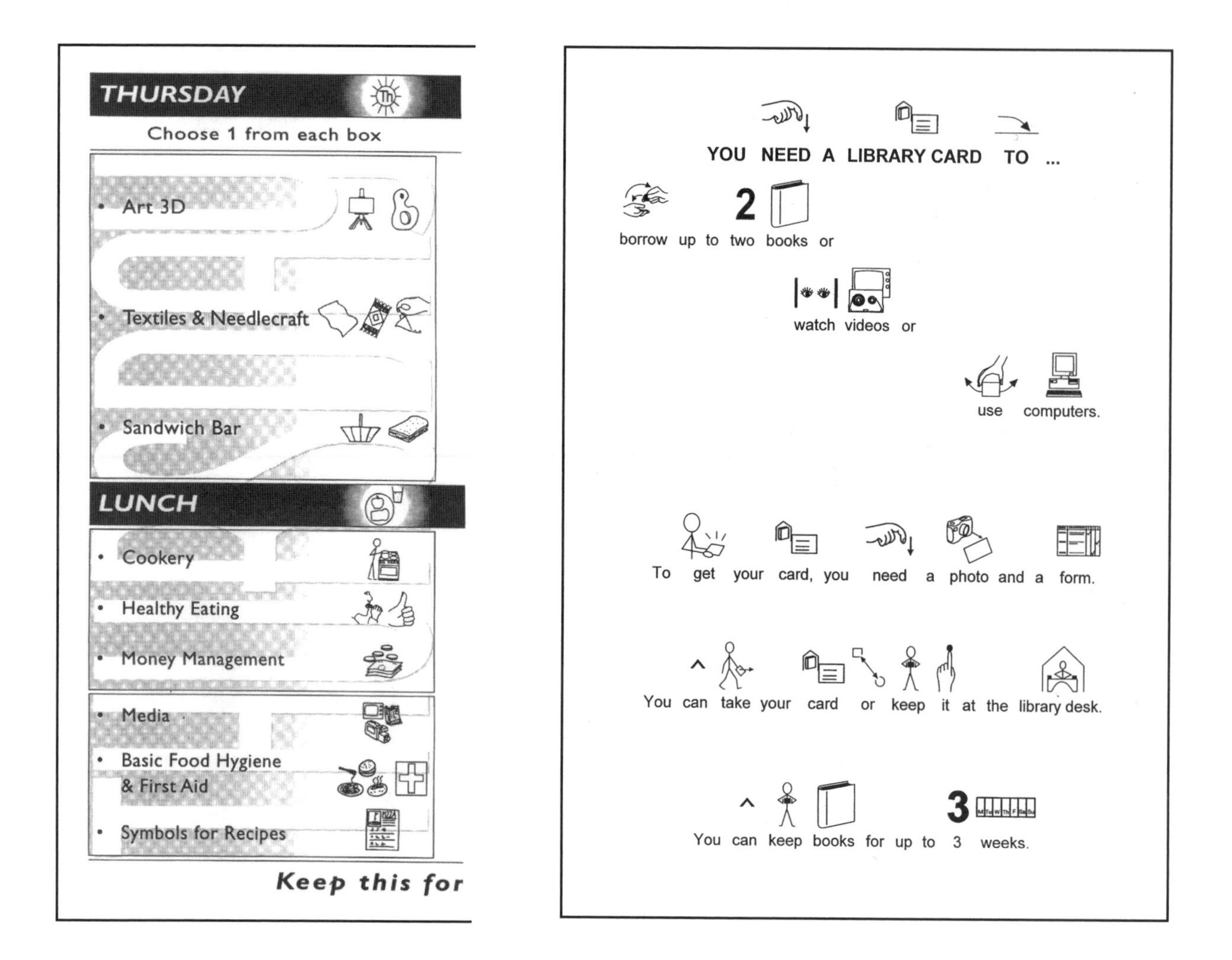


*Two styles of information resource, one formal, the other informal. The informal uses a higher level of symbol support.*

Bev Vaughan, also at the Isle of Wight college, has developed symbolised focus pages on the college Intranet. This means that students are able to access pages on cookery, music, arts and sport, these also provide quick links to Internet web pages.

A resource pack has been developed by the Learning Disability Service in South Devon in conjunction with Cruse Bereavement Care (South Devon). This pack has sections dealing with issues such as visiting an undertaker, going to a funeral, feelings and loss. The pack also contains useful signs and symbols for supporting communication on this topic.

There are many organisations producing information which uses symbols, and any list here will be out of date as son as it is published. The Internet is a good source of information.

**Summary**

Symbol users benefit from information being provided in symbol format as it is often more accessible

Information provided in symbol format promotes symbol users autonomy

Being able to access information can help people prepare for new experiences and events.

Care is needed in creating symbol supported information so that it is accessible to a range of readers.

# CHAPTER 6

## SUPPORTING INCLUSION WITH SYMBOLS

**Symbols can enable and encourage both students and workers with learning disabilities to be more included in school life and more productive in the workplace. Symbols can also assist people with learning disabilities to take part more fully in events in the wider community.**

**Information presented via symbols can assist in the development of self-advocacy by providing prompts or reminders.**

**Self-advocacy can also be promoted by using symbols in questionnaires for service users regarding service delivery. The feedback users provide can play an important part in the development and improvement of services they use.**

➤ The symbol project in Oldham aims to develop the use of symbols in the general community to enable people who don't read to have access to information. The focus of the group has gradually changed from developing symbols for day centres to offering support in the wider community. The group hoped that by influencing the community at large, some of the barriers which are disabling, might be broken. The group decided to target the Royal Oldham Hospital, as an example of a situation that would greatly benefit from having symbols incorporated into signposts and literature.

In collaboration with the hospital, the group set up a pilot to test if symbols would work in this context. The pilot study focused on six departments that were reported to be the most difficult for patients to find. They started by evaluating how well users could find these departments given the current information.

Over a period of time the group worked to develop suitable symbols. They used a range of sources, including clip-art images. Jessica Tuck and Alison Matthews, writing up the project, say:

> "One of the problems we had with symbols design was the fact that we were not familiar with the work of each department, and we were well aware our symbols might have reflected a stereotypical image rather than a true one. In designing our symbols we wanted to strike a balance

> between accuracy and appropriateness on the one hand, and simplicity with consequent ease of reproduction and recognition on the other. One of the things we realised was that we needed more input from staff in the actual departments."

After trialling their new symbols a presentation was made to senior managers of the trust. The presentation involved service users as well as project staff. The presentation was very successful and as a result the trust agreed:

- to increase the use of internationally recognised symbols (e.g. for information points, restaurants etc);
- to involve the symbol group in some of the re-signing work planned
- to identify a small budget to allow for some further re-signing with symbols elsewhere on the site.

> "A symbol design session was arranged involving representatives from the hospital, and people with a learning disability. A graphic designer was available to help to interpret peoples' suggestions, and members of hospital staff were encouraged to consult with colleagues in order to ensure that all members of staff were happy with the design.
>
> The design session produced an assortment of ideas and styles, which can be seen in the final symbols. For example both two- and three-dimensional images have been used. During the process it became apparent that a sense of ownership by the departments was more important than standardisation of symbols (for example by using Rebus conventions).
>
> In April 1999 the new signposts complete with symbols were installed. The introduction of symbols is undoubtedly a positive step towards real inclusion."

This is not the only context where symbol development is taking place. The Speech and Language Therapy service have also been involved with a project with Greater Manchester Transport Executive to improve access to public transport. A transport workshop took place as part of the year 2000 Total Communication Conference. The success of these initiatives is in part due to the inclusion of symbol users as designers as well as consumers.

| | | |
|---|---|---|
| Café Royal | CT Scan | Day Services Unit |
| Information Centre | Intensive Therapy Unit | MRI |
| Pharmacy | Ultrasound | X-Ray |

*Some of the symbols created by the symbol group for The Royal Oldham Hospital.*

## Inclusion in Education

➤ Justin Drew from Glebefields Health Centre, is concerned that the student's needs are placed before the needs of the school.

> "Working alongside the new educational model of **'inclusion'** we need to be modifying the environment to support the child. This has always been my approach. However, many schools even now are still adopting an **'integration'** model where by they try to change the child to suit the environment. With regards to symbols many schools adopt one symbol system (e.g. Rebus) over another (e.g. PCS) to meet the needs of the school rather than the needs of the child. This is poor teaching practice. However, when I have pointed this out many teachers realise that this is indeed what they are doing, and that they are failing the needs of their students.
>
> I have found many a light bulb go off in peoples heads

when I explain this approach to them with a realisation that this important educational model is not being met by many schools in their use of symbols. It is also the most valid way of moving forward in the communication and learning methods for the students we work with - suit the symbol to the needs of the student."

## Newspapers, and community publications

➤ Students at a George Hastwell School in Cumbria produce a newspaper each term where many of the articles are accompanied by symbols. The students are given a high level of editorial control over the content and this is an empowering experience. They are responsible for the process of gathering material, writing articles, taking digital photographs, carrying out surveys and making decisions about what should and should not be included.

When the articles are gathered together, the process of cutting and pasting to make up the pages begins. The photocopier is used to make further adjustments to the size of individual articles as the jigsaw puzzle of each A3 sized page is completed. By keeping this activity practical and by using real, rather than digital, scissors and glue the whole process of assembling the newspaper remains within the students' control. When all the pages are finished they are photocopied, collated and stapled together for distribution.

The school reduces one copy to A4 size and then laminates and binds the pages. This archive copy is kept in the library with earlier editions, a growing resource that documents the history of the pupils and the school.

The newspaper enjoys a wide readership outside the school community. The fact that so many people appreciate it has served to further raise the students' self-esteem. It also increases awareness of the power of symbols amongst non-symbol usere. It is interesting to note that the presentation of traditional orthography with symbols ensures the inclusion of the non-symbol literate! Copies of the paper have circulated to many countries world-wide, including India and South Africa. In this way the newspaper has become a goodwill ambassador for symbols, crossing international boundaries.

➤ News-4-You is an internet newspaper service produced exclusively for the special needs classroom, and has proven to be a tool that teachers and therapists world-wide are using to augment their functional curriculums. News-4-You uses a symbols-supported text to discuss current events, a discussion that serves to expand, motivate and encourage a broader individual learning

*A page from the Sprint 2000 edition of the George Hastwell Newspaper created by an editorial team of students.*

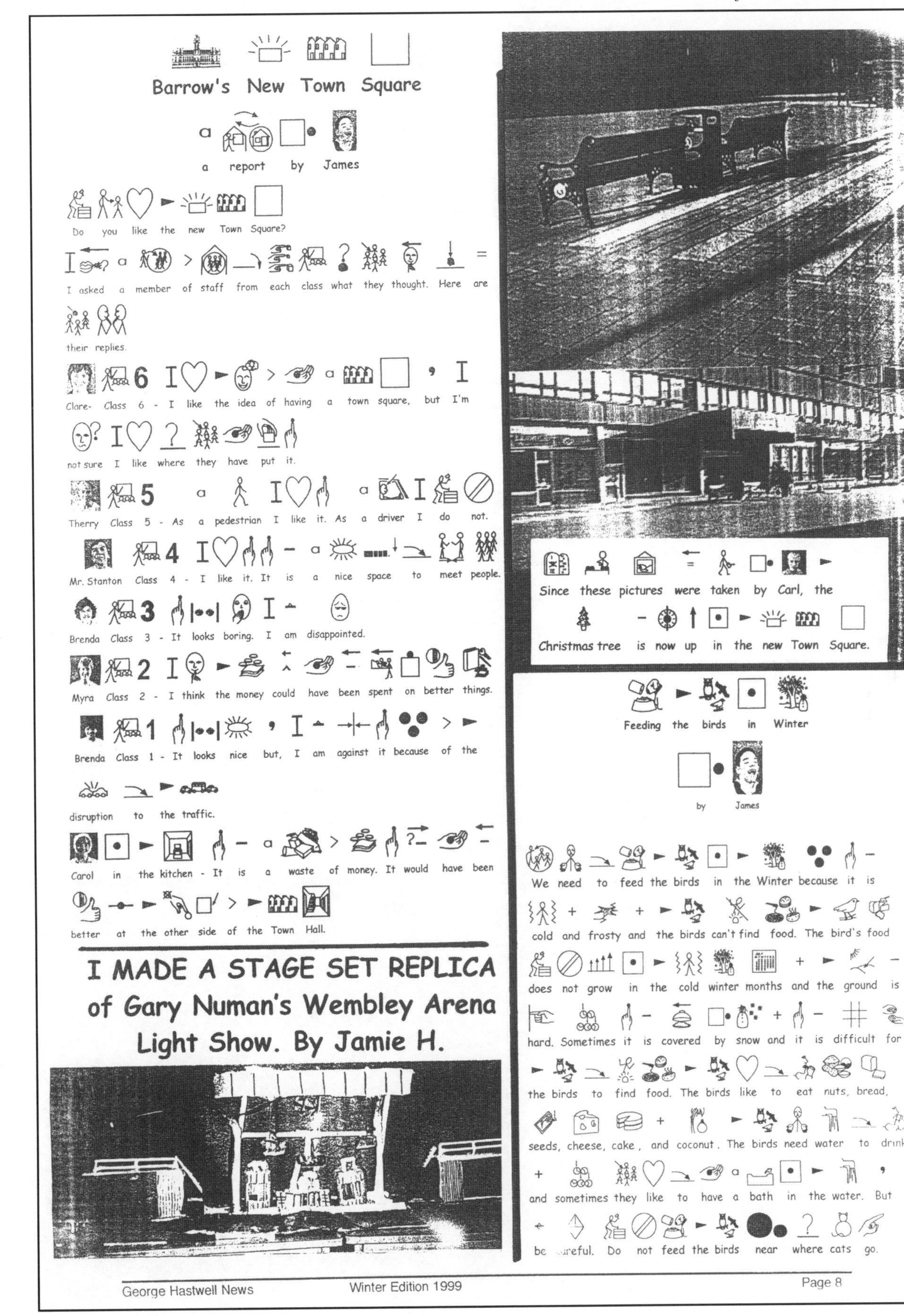

## Barrow's New Town Square

a report by James

Do you like the new Town Square?

I asked a member of staff from each class what they thought. Here are their replies.

Clare- Class 6 - I like the idea of having a town square, but I'm not sure I like where they have put it.

Therry Class 5 - As a pedestrian I like it. As a driver I do not.

Mr. Stanton Class 4 - I like it. It is a nice space to meet people.

Brenda Class 3 - It looks boring. I am disappointed.

Myra Class 2 - I think the money could have been spent on better things.

Brenda Class 1 - It looks nice but, I am against it because of the disruption to the traffic.

Carol in the kitchen - It is a waste of money. It would have been better at the other side of the Town Hall.

Since these pictures were taken by Carl, the Christmas tree is now up in the new Town Square.

## Feeding the birds in Winter

by James

We need to feed the birds in the Winter because it is cold and frosty and the birds can't find food. The bird's food does not grow in the cold winter months and the ground is hard. Sometimes it is covered by snow and it is difficult for the birds to find food. The birds like to eat nuts, bread, seeds, cheese, cake, and coconut. The birds need water to drink and sometimes they like to have a bath in the water. But be careful. Do not feed the birds near where cats go.

## I MADE A STAGE SET REPLICA of Gary Numan's Wembley Arena Light Show. By Jamie H.

George Hastwell News Winter Edition 1999 Page 8

base, and greater engagement with society.

It is published weekly from September to June. Each week it covers one current topic. They attempt to give enough information about the topic (what, who and where pages) to enable the students to relate to others. There is a joke page, game page, recipe page, quiz page and vocabulary page all of which reinforce the weekly topic. At the end of the newspaper they include extra pages about other outstanding news or updates on previously reported issues.

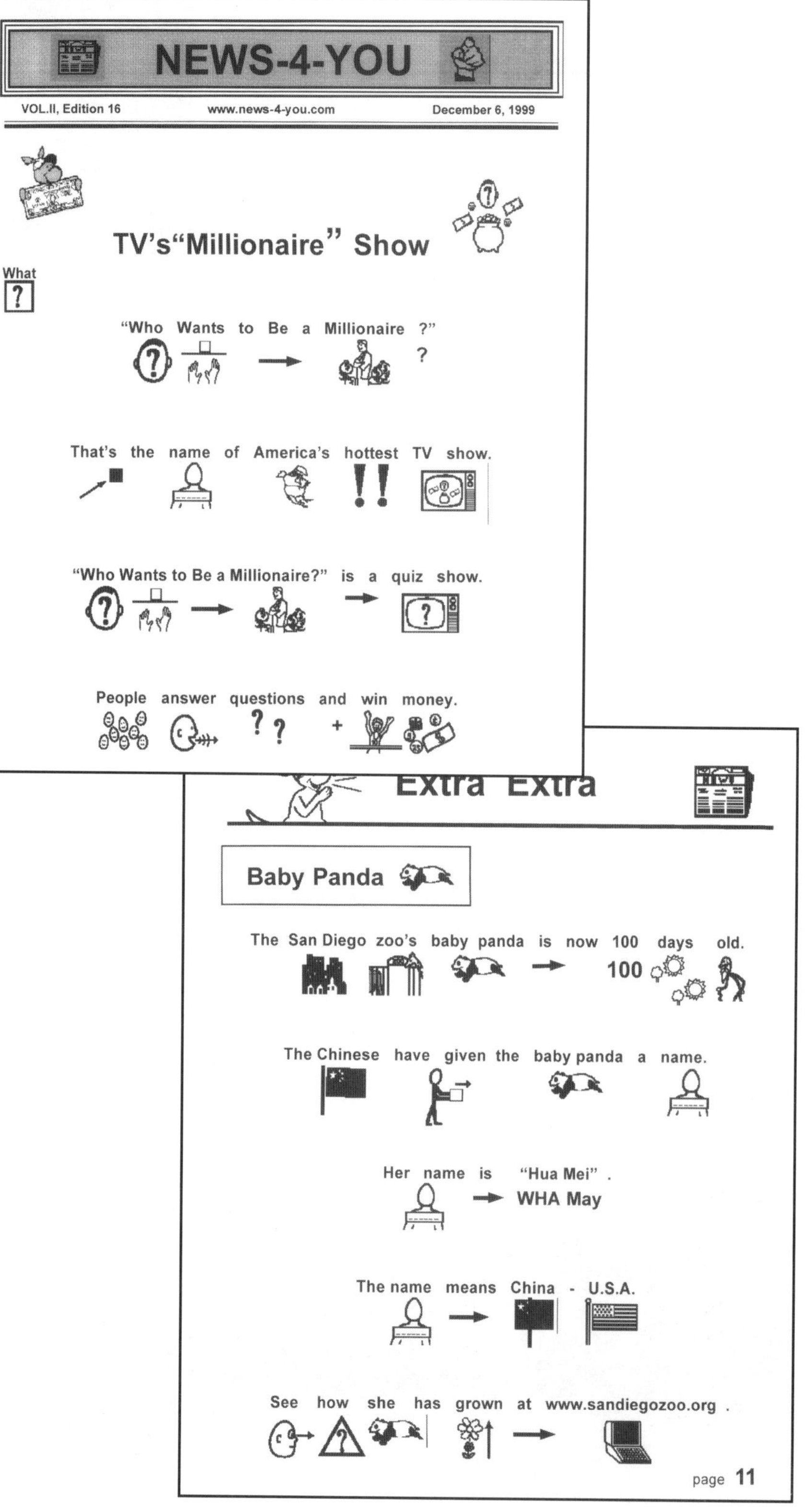

NEWS-4-YOU

VOL.II, Edition 16 www.news-4-you.com December 6, 1999

TV's "Millionaire" Show

What

"Who Wants to Be a Millionaire ?"

That's the name of America's hottest TV show.

"Who Wants to Be a Millionaire?" is a quiz show.

People answer questions and win money.

Extra Extra

Baby Panda

The San Diego zoo's baby panda is now 100 days old.

100

The Chinese have given the baby panda a name.

Her name is "Hua Mei" .

WHA May

The name means China - U.S.A.

See how she has grown at www.sandiegozoo.org .

page 11

*Two pages from one edition of the News-4-You newspaper.*

*An extract from the journal, Respect. Respect contains articles from a variety of people – religious education teachers as well as young students with learning disabilities.*

➤ Respect is a journal edited by Erica Brown for people interested in Christian Education. Articles are included at a variety of language levels including symbol articles. The aim is to make all readers feel included in the journal, even if they can't read everything.

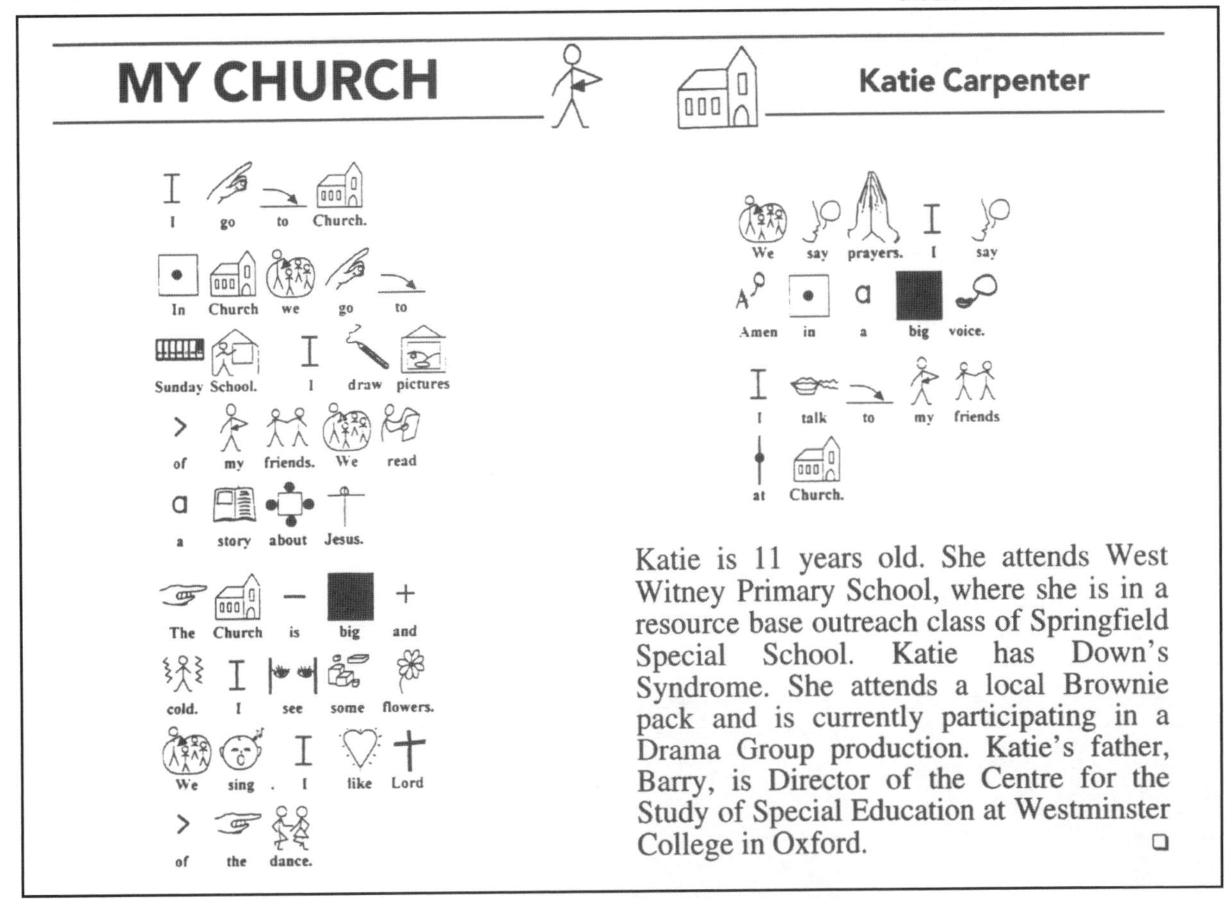

**MY CHURCH**

**Katie Carpenter**

I go to Church. In Church we go to Sunday School. I draw pictures of my friends. We read a story about Jesus.

The Church is big and cold. I see some flowers. We sing. I like Lord of the dance.

We say prayers. I say Amen in a big voice. I talk to my friends at Church.

Katie is 11 years old. She attends West Witney Primary School, where she is in a resource base outreach class of Springfield Special School. Katie has Down's Syndrome. She attends a local Brownie pack and is currently participating in a Drama Group production. Katie's father, Barry, is Director of the Centre for the Study of Special Education at Westminster College in Oxford. ❑

➤ At Watergate School in south-east London, staff have worked with Widgit Software on the design and development of symbols to assist in teaching Religious Education to students with learning difficulties. Some of the symbols were abstract ones to denote the major faiths of Christianity, Islam, Sikhism, Judaism, Buddhism and Hinduism. These symbols used the particular icons of each of the religions. Other symbols related to particular characters in some of the narratives associated with each faith, for example they use images of St Francis from Christianity, the story of David and Goliath from Judaism, the baby Krishna from Hinduism and symbols indicating how everyone is equal before God in Sikhism.

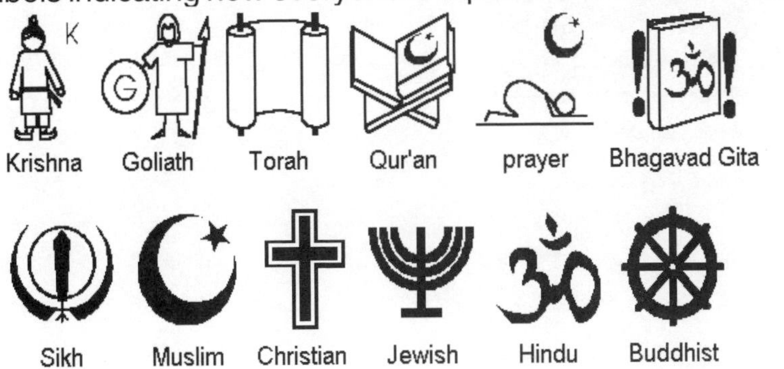


*Symbols for different faiths..*

## Inclusion in the workplace

➤ The Forum @ Greenwich is a community centre that runs a café project for people with learning difficulties. Workers at the café are helped with symbols on the menu board when taking orders, on notices and signs. Rebus symbols are also used in training materials covering issues such as catering hygiene and life skills. The text on the wall of the café which tells customers about the project has also been symbolised. Having the information available publicly demonstrates the capabilities of the staff to customers, and helps to support the inclusive ethos.

➤ Keith Bates from Pathway Employment has produced a number of information leaflets to facilitate inclusion in the workplace. For example there are information sheets on how to lift, complaints procedures etc. These are illustrated in Chapter 5, Accessing Information.

➤ Rebecca, described in Chapter 1, used communication books with photographs and symbols to help her in her work experience. Without this aid colleagues unfamiliar with people who have learning disabilities would have found difficulties working with Rebecca. As it was, these strategies aiding communication transformed the workplace.

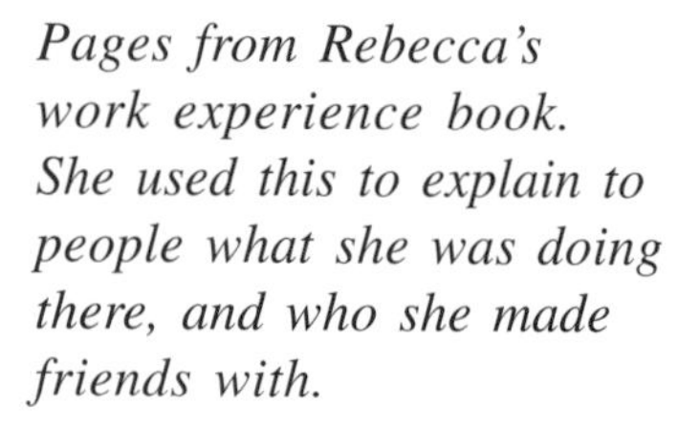
*Pages from Rebecca's work experience book. She used this to explain to people what she was doing there, and who she made friends with.*

## Inclusion in the Community

➤ George and Eileen Lindley have developed a series of symbolised bible stories and other resources to support christian symbol users. The stories cover the major gospel stories as well as concepts such as prayer. These stories were made for the local church so that all children could participate in church activities. George and Eileen have set up a small business to share these and other resources to help others achieve the same objectives.

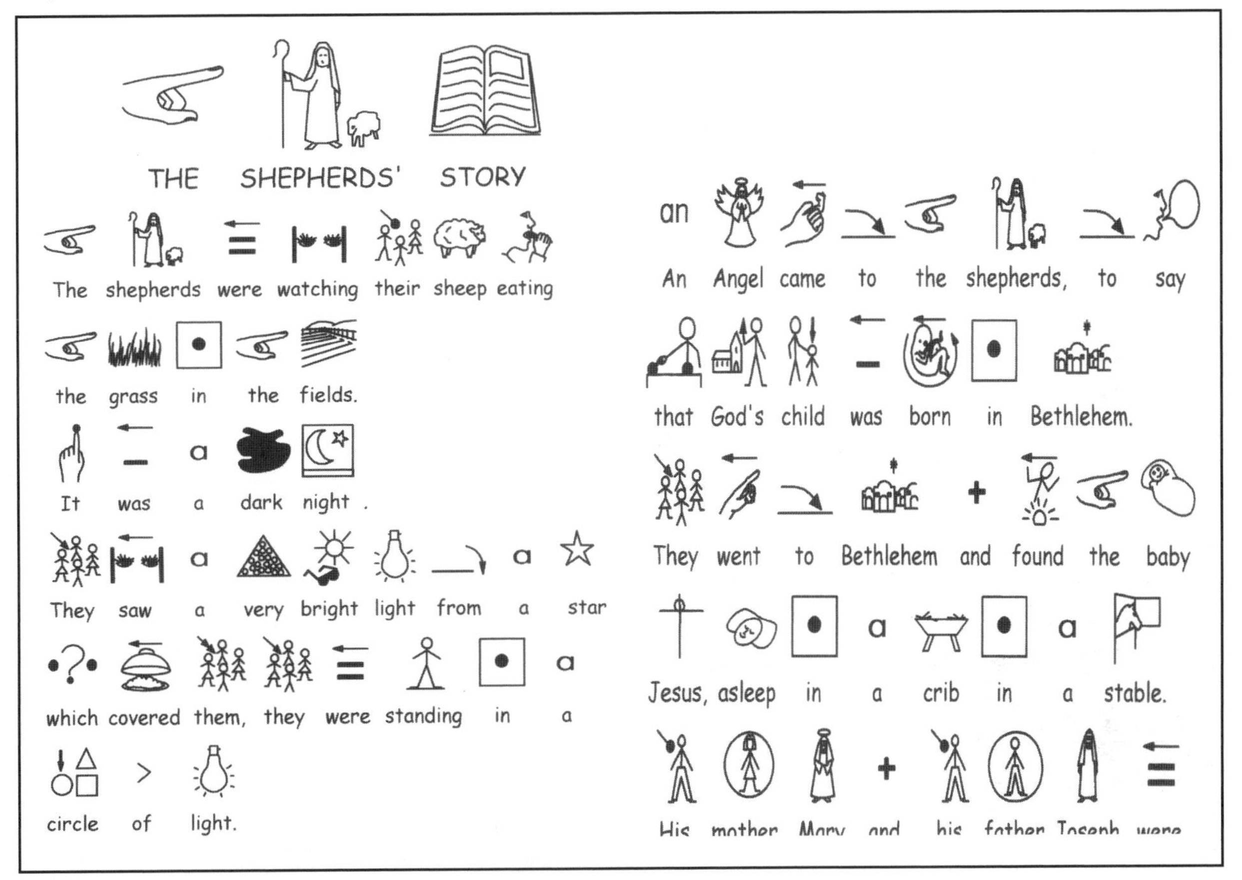


➤ When a memorial service was held to celebrate the lives of four friends who had attended the Mill Lane Centre, Barrow-In-Furness, the order of service was symbolised. The four people had died in tragic circumstances during a narrow-boat holiday and every care was taken to ensure that their relatives, friends and colleagues from the centre, who attended the service, would be able to follow and take part in the service.

The order of the service was introduced with a symbolised summary of what was going to happen and symbolised directions for what the congregation was to do. Two of the five hymns were symbolised in full, the other three were not amenable to the addition of symbols and so, instead, a symbolised synopsis was provided. This strategy meant that the one order of service book was suitable for the whole congregation.

It was designed and produced to such a high standard that the booklet itself became not only a marvellous example of the inclusiveness of symbols but also one of the many memorials to these four friends.

*The symbols in this order of service help participation by explaining what is happening.*

We Sing ... 'the Lord's My Shepherd'.

This hymn tells us how God looks after us

and gives us all we need. Then when we

die, he takes us to be with him.

The Lord's my shepherd, I'll not want;
He makes me down to lie
In pastures green; he leadeth me
The quiet waters by.

My soul he doth restore again,
And me to walk doth make
Within the paths of righteousness,
E'en for his own name's sake.

Yea, though I walk in death's dark vale,
Yet will I fear no ill:
For thou art with me, and thy rod
And staff me comfort still.

My table thou hast furnishèd
In presence of my foes;
My head thou dost with oil anoint
And my cup overflows.

➤ Adam regularly used symbols. He used symbols for communication at school and also at home with his family. He would often arrive at school on a Monday morning with his symbolised personal weekend news report, compiled by Adam with his father's help on the computer keyboard.

When Adam died it seemed appropriate and natural to use symbols on the service sheets for his funeral mass. This not only included Adam's school friends in the service, it also made a strong statement about Adam and the importance of symbols for him and his family.

Adam has symbols on his headstone on a hillside in Cumbria, overlooking Morecambe Bay, a suitably prominent position for such a remarkable young man. The symbols say "Loved and remembered always".

*Symbols can make a strong statement.*

## Using symbols to empower and support learners

Making oneself heard is difficult for many people, but can be almost impossible for some symbol users. By sensitive and appropriate use of symbols, however, not only can their views be heard but they can also often be empowered to participate in self advocacy.

### Using symbols to support advocacy

➤ The Communication Therapy Team at Lea Castle Centre produced a symbolised version of the services leaflet for the Wolverley area in Worcestershire. The leaflet used symbols and words to explain the services offered by the communication therapy team. This included information on respite services, information, day services and home meetings. The team set up a symbol group to simplify and translate client needs into symbolised form, a service that would be extremely valuable if it were to be available everywhere rather than just in certain locations. Among the resources symbolised for clients have been timetables, care plans, recipes, shopping lists, fire procedures and how to complain. This group has also worked to develop a common approach to the choice of symbols used across the region.

➤ Ian Burtenshaw works at St Piers, the national centre for young people with epilepsy. He was involved in symbolising a survey form for a research project looking at the benefits of the twenty-four hour curriculum in residential schools. The survey asked students for their feelings about school, teachers, curriculum and visits out of school. The survey was followed by a tick list of activities offered in some schools. The survey questions and the tick-list items were all symbolised.

*A survey to gather student's views.*

### Symbols enabling self-advocacy

➤ In Hounslow, west London, the Self Advocacy Project for Adults with Learning Difficulties worked with Railtrack on their disability strategy. They produced a symbolised booklet explaining the policy and how it relates to the requirements for all public bodies. The booklet was produced in order to gather the views of a wide range of disabled users of the railway, and responses could be submitted by telephone, minicom, fax or email.

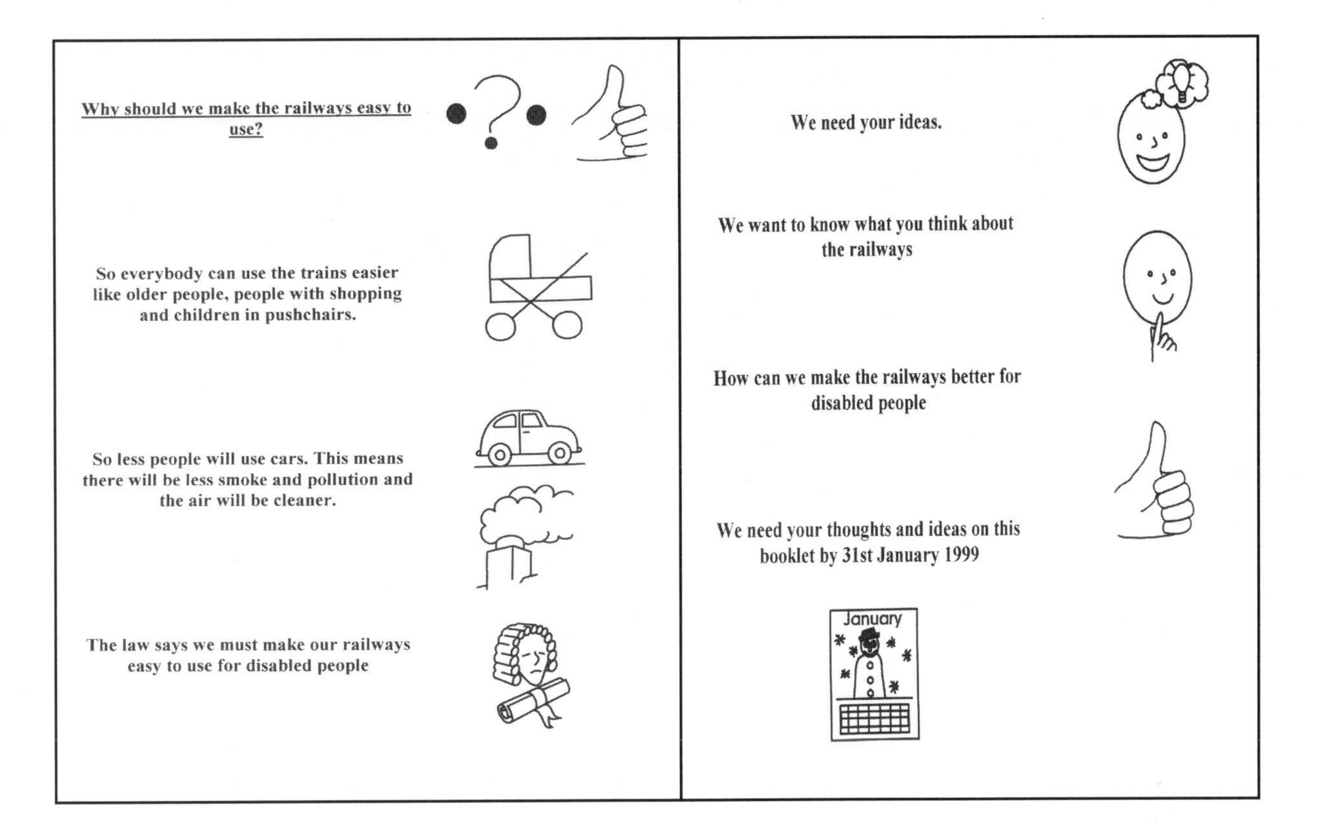


➤ Jo Coulson-Davis works for Royal Association for Deaf People (RAD) and is involved in helping those people who are deaf or hard of hearing. Jo has produced many resources, including advice on using hearing aids as well as social information. As a hearing impaired person, Jo is aware of the some of the language difficulties that deaf people experience, and of issues such as tenses which are handled differently by symbols and signing. She is interested in symbol development, and the current discussions on how signing and symbol language structures could converge. Her aim is to help deaf people feel and become more included in all aspects of life.

Jo is a member of the Surrey Symbols Working Group, described in Chapter 4. Collaboration between many different groups in the county has led to an improvement in the quality of accessible information and therefore to more inclusive support.

➤ In Devon, the Total Communication Partnership has produced a number of leaflets to help service-users become involved in self-advocacy. The complaints form produced by the Partnership takes up two sides of an A4 page and is designed for users who can access some text. Boxes are provided for answers that mostly consist of completing sentences. Symbols appear alongside the questions to communicate alongside the written word-based text.

It is not the usual practice at the Total Communication Network to use the symbols to support words; it is more usual that a symbol or picture will be chosen as the main communicating device, and appropriate words will then be attached to ensure that all those accessing the text will understand it. The address for the form to be sent back to is not just listed but shown written on an envelope complete with stamp, providing a symbolised support in itself.

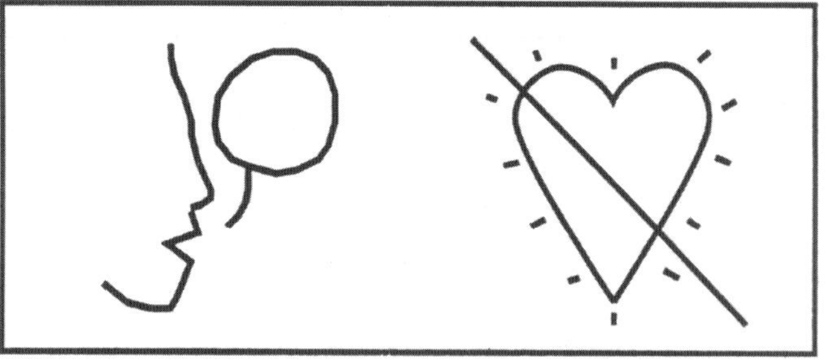

Say what you don't like

Not far away, in Bristol, Real Voice Media are involved in using symbols to present community care plans, magazines, constitutions, charters, child protection documentation, minutes, evaluations and letters. An increasing number of organisations are adding symbols to their publications with the intention of including more readers.

**Summary**

Symbols encourage people with learning disabilities to be more included in social settings e.g. at school and in the workplace.

The use of symbols can help workers to be more effective and productive in the workplace.

Symbols can help user's take part more fully in important ceremonies and transitions in life.

Symbols can help in the development of self-advocacy by providing prompts or reminders.

Symbolised information enables users to make full use of services available.

Symbolised information assists users in providing valuable feedback for development and improvement or related services.

# CHAPTER 7

## LITERACY, LITERATURE AND SYMBOLS

**The use of symbols can open the wider world of literature to those who cannot access it through traditional text. Similarly, symbols can be used to make libraries and other resources more accessible to people with learning disabilities. Symbols may also be used to assist users in responding to various texts and articulate their feelings.**

**Using symbols can open doors to people with autism and similar learning disabilities to both a wealth of resources and communication that, without symbols could otherwise be prohibitive.**

**Many schools have recognised the benefits of using symbols with their pupils and some are choosing to use symbols as part of the National Literacy and Numeracy Frameworks. Recording a students work in symbolised form enables them to understand and be involved in their progress.**

➤ In May 1998 George Hastwell School, in Barrow-in-Furness, was one of seven special schools invited to submit a bid to trial a Literacy Summer School for pupils with learning difficulties. The bid had to ensure a minimum of fifty hours intensive literacy tuition, the same requirement applied to mainstream schools wishing to arrange summer schools. This was an extremely challenging requirement. However, teachers were confident they could meet the requirements because of their experience of using symbols to support literacy. The bid was successful and the school arranged a summer school for 13 pupils. Ten pupils from the special school were enrolled alongside three from local mainstream schools.

When the document outlining the *National Literacy Strategy* [DfEE 1998] had been introduced it was noticeable that it had very few references to pupils with special educational needs. However, the supplementary guidance, which appeared some months later, highlighted how symbols can be used to support implementation of the Strategy with pupils who have learning disabilities. Teaching and learning materials included in the *Activity Resource Sheets* [DfEE 1998], a part of the Literacy

Strategy training pack, contained examples of how symbols can be used effectively to support activities during the literacy hour.

Symbols can be used to support the development of phonological and grammatical awareness, and an understanding of print, all of which are areas of work identified within the *National Literacy Strategy.* Worksheets accompanied by symbols provide a useful method of developing and assessing reading comprehension.

The range of activities was designed to be wide, engaging and fully supported by symbols. The intensity of the programme allowed the build up of literary momentum!

The school is in Cumbria and so the theme of Lakeland Writers was adopted. This provided the pupils with opportunities to read from, and to learn more about, writers who have lived in Cumbria, like Beatrix Potter, Arthur Ransome and William and Dorothy Wordsworth. The theme was also significant because it recognised the pupils as Lakeland Writers themselves. The theme of Lakeland Writers meant that it was possible to plan literacy focussed visits within reasonable travelling distance of the school. Visits were arranged to Furness Abbey; Dove Cottage, a cottage shared by the Wordsworths in Grasmere; and Hill Top, the first lakeland farm bought by Beatrix Potter. The pupils also visited Ottakars, a local bookshop, in order to choose books in exchange for the book tokens they had been given.

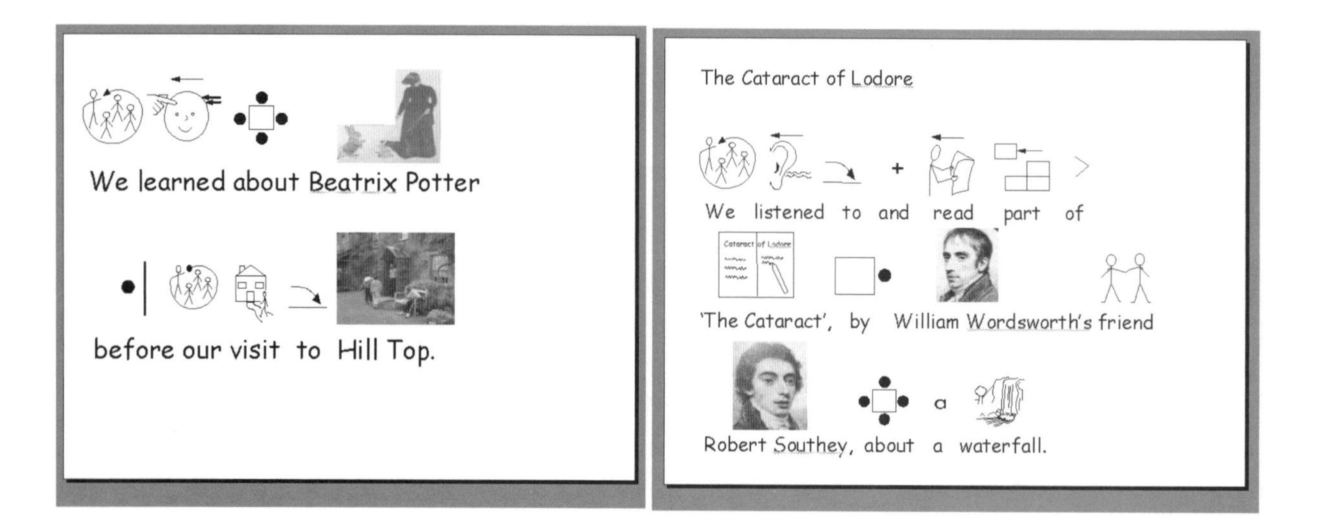


Throughout the summer school the pupils had access to high levels of staff support and imaginative teaching. Information and communication technologies were used to the full and each day began with a review of the pictures taken the previous day. The pictures were taken with a digital camera and put into Powerpoint [Microsoft] presentations. A line of text for *shared reading* accompanied each picture. The pupils were delighted to see the pictures and texts projected via a digital/video projector onto a large white wall in the sensory room. Having everyone sitting comfortably together on the floor, in semi-darkness, watching, reading, thinking, listening and talking provided a high technology...but nonetheless magic...lantern show.

The fact that it is possible to symbolise well known stories and poems, and to include symbols in presentations about the lives of famous Lakeland authors, ensured that the pupils were included in areas of learning which would have been much harder, if not impossible, to access without symbols. For example, Wordsworth's poem *Daffodils* was accompanied by symbols, projected and read, collectively, by the group. Some of the less obvious symbols were soon learned, and subsequently remembered, by pupils who have this well-known fragment of English literature for their own personal, future use.

We all write the story together on the big screen.

Visits to Furness Abbey, Dove Cottage and Hill Top were motivating as well as informative. Presenters dressed in costume provided activities at an appropriate level, making visits both magical and memorable for both pupils and staff.

Every afternoon when the pupils were in school and not on an educational visit they engaged in a drama activity in the sensory room. The story was loosely based on the Arthur Ransome story of *Swallow and Amazons.* They began by talking about what had happened during their adventure. The words that had been used during the sessions had been recorded and these helped to stimulate the discussion. The staff talked about describing words, how they were used in writing stories and the group wrote the adventure story together using Writing with Symbols on a computer connected to the data projector. As pupils suggested words they were typed and instantly appeared, projected onto a large white wall.
During this shared writing task the group talked about how

sentences begin with capital letters and end with either a full stop or other punctuation mark. Pupils were generally very responsive during these sessions including those who would have usually been too shy to contribute. This may have been because of the anonymity of the semi-darkened room and/or the significance of seeing their words appear on the wall and hearing the computer read them. The teaching and learning technologies in this environment made the activity particularly engaging and compelling.

The summer school was a delightful, memorable and unique experience for everyone who became involved in it. It would not have been possible to be so adventurous without ready and reliable access to the support of symbols.

## Sources of literature

Although there are few published symbol texts, many teachers are creating their own symbol supported stories.

*A page from an Oxford Reading Tree Story recreated with symbols.*

Literary texts are not always in book form however, and newspapers and magazine are also part of the literate world. On Track is a newspaper produced at Westminster College and which makes extensive use of Rebus symbols. Some of the symbolised texts included in On Track are quite long and may extend over several A3 pages. Symbol use is often intended for clients who may be able to cope with only a short text, but On Track shows that others can access long and more complex texts in this way. There are also some word-based texts and photographs in the newspaper, which reports on activities over a wide area of the midlands. Guest editorial boards come from some of the special schools in the area whose activities form the articles, and they work alongside representatives of schools and of MENCAP, who supported the publication.

## Symbols, the SEN Code of Practice and the Literacy and Numeracy Frameworks

➤ Symbols have unlocked literacy for many young pupils. Judy Wood at Springfield School remembers how one young four year old pupil was very excited when the computer was able to read back to him phrases which meant something. In his case, explains Judy, that meant Cartoon Network, Star Wars, Johnny Bravo or Fox Kids.

> 'He types into the computer and loves it when each letter is spoken. He listens and has learnt when he needs to use backspace – he sometimes lingers too long on a letter – it's wonderful to see him at work.'

➤ Anne McKelvey teaches at Northfield School in York, and uses symbols to support and develop communication and literacy. Pupils at the school are aged from three to sixteen, and have a wide range of special educational needs. Many of their needs relate to speech and language difficulties. Northfield uses a mixture of the different symbol sets depending on the child. Literacy support with symbols includes symbolised stories, symbol cloze procedure tasks and symbol-sequencing tasks for those with reading difficulties. Symbols are also used at Northfield on signs and labels around the school, for timetables and choice cards, for children with Autistic Spectrum Disorder and in the school's use of PECS. As Anne says,

> 'Use of symbols has opened up new opportunities in communication and understanding for many children with SEN. They are brilliant!'

➤ At the Hadrian Education Centre in Tyne and Wear, Carol Allen has developed other ways of using symbols to support literacy. She uses a basic text which has been symbolised together with a range of story starters which can help students to continue the story themselves.

Carol explains,

> 'It's a structured way of extending a basic storyline to give it some depth. The questions are not comprehension as the answers are not to be found only in the text. The idea is for students to elaborate and extend; to become descriptive if possible and finally to continue the story and then evaluate their ideas against a suggested conclusion.'

As Carol suggests, not totally seriously, this is almost an early developmental version of literary criticism.

Carol also has a number of strategies for encouraging creative writing, and helping pupils over 'creative blocks'. For example, she puts pictures and symbols on large dice or cubes. Roll the dice to get a suggestion for the next idea in your story. This is better than getting a teacher to suggest – but gives choices within a manageable range. Alternatively, make cards with pictures or symbols to be picked from a box or bag.

Sometimes a reluctant write can be encouraged by co-operation. Jo Egerton encouraged The Attack of the Carrots through an interview technique, which drew out the writer's creativity. Knowing the article was to be published also helped to encourage writing. Outcomes can affect a writer's willingness to complete their work.

*An article for a newspaper, using interview as a means of stimulating creativity.*

# Attack of the Carrots

## Designing a Maths Trail

➤ In designing a maths trail at Meldreth Manor School, the maths co-ordinator, Hazel, wanted to ensure that the greatest possible accessibility was built into the process. This implied careful consideration of the use of open ended maths problems within the trail, which could be differentiated both within level one and across levels one and two, and through the integration of symbols into the trail itself. Symbols are well embedded into practice at the school and finding a range of symbol labelled spaces to work from was no problem. The notion that only the key information carrying words within a problem was to be augmented with symbols was discussed with the speech therapy team.

**Measure a pet**

Can you find a pet to measure?

You will need to use the string.

Stretch the string from your pet's nose to the end of its tail.

Now cut it off.

(The string NOT the pet's tail!)

stretch it around your pet's tummy.

label both pieces of string - tummy and length

Bring both pieces of string to school.

Bring a photo or drawing of your pet.

However, additional problems emerged as the trail developed: sometimes the symbols gave the pupil additional clues and made the concepts being taught and tested less complex than had been intended. To give an example, when pupils were asked to identify a geometric shape within an environment, the symbol for shape appears to give them three options to compare the environment with, rather than asking them to recall shape names and match them against a cognitive image of that shape. Some of these problems were irreconcilable and a compromise had to be reached: however, they emphasize the problems that can emerge in integrating alternative and augmentative communication (AAC) with a subject which uses symbols within its own vocabulary.

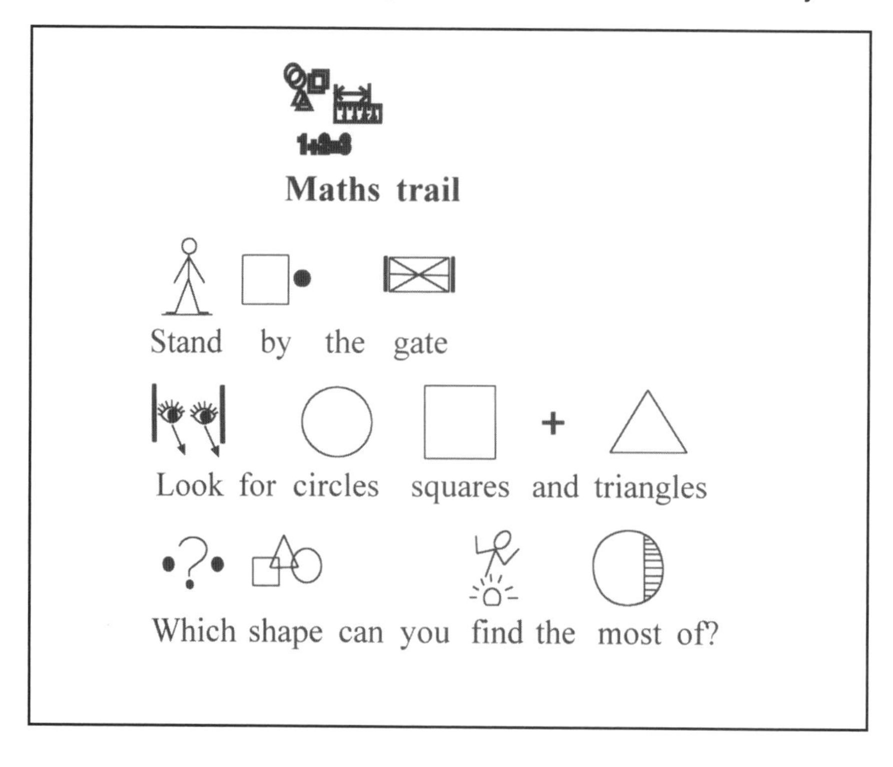


## Using symbols to become literate and to enjoy literature

Symbols can be a means of accessing literate worlds which would otherwise be closed to some. By using symbols to support or replace traditional word-based texts, some of those heritage texts can be made more accessible. The process of becoming literate, too, can be enhanced and supported by the use of symbols.

➤ Students at George Hastwell School used their own puppets to act a modified version of *The Tempest*. They made puppets for the characters which were photographed to go with symbols in their copy of the play. Everybody in the class had a part. The video showed how engaged the students were in the drama, showing that there are many plays and stories from literature which have a place in today's education and entertainment.

➤ Carol Allen's students are also exploring poetry with the aid of symbols:

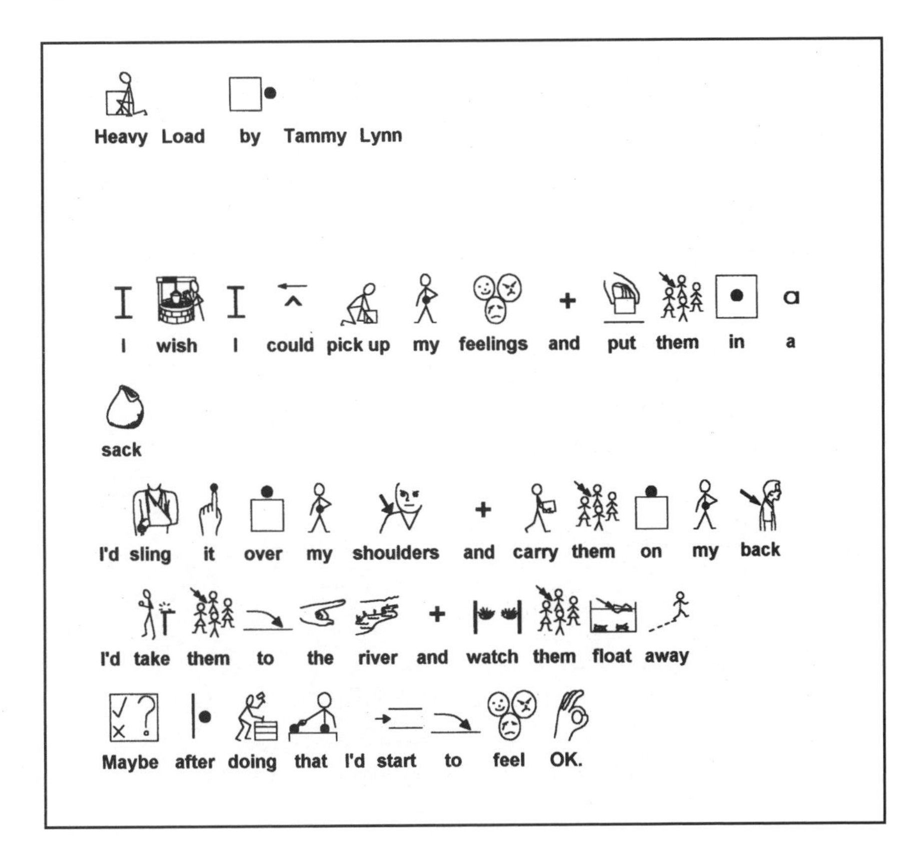

## The Literacy Hour

The Literacy Hour has been made more accessible to students with autism and/or severe learning difficulties by using symbols to give meaning to text, and to help hyperlexic students (those who can read the words but have no understanding of their meaning) to understand what the text is about. Symbols, whether in the form of photos, pictures or line drawings, are an excellent way to introduce words, or communication. For some students whose communication is at a very early stage this may be teaching them that the symbol for cup relates to a real cup and that they can use this to ask for a drink by giving it to a friend, family member or member of staff, depending on where they are.

Symbols supporting the text help the pupils to work with complex issues, and demonstrate that the issues are within their grasp. The symbols mean that they are not excluded by reason of text.

Sarah has worked with students with severe learning difficulties, and one student, Stephen, who shows many difficulties common to dyslexia, has been helped enormously by the use of symbols with text. His self esteem has increased as he has realised that he can learn to read - he had thought he was "stupid" because he couldn't read even simple words. Other students with severe learning difficulties have been using symbols to begin to construct simple sentences, even to retell simple stories they have been working on during the Literacy Hour.

➤ George and Eileen Lindley have made a number of literacy activity packs for the key vocabulary. Books with matching cards aid symbol and word recognition, and flash cards with symbols help in matching and recognition games.

*Flash cards and matching activities can help word recognition and vocabulary.*

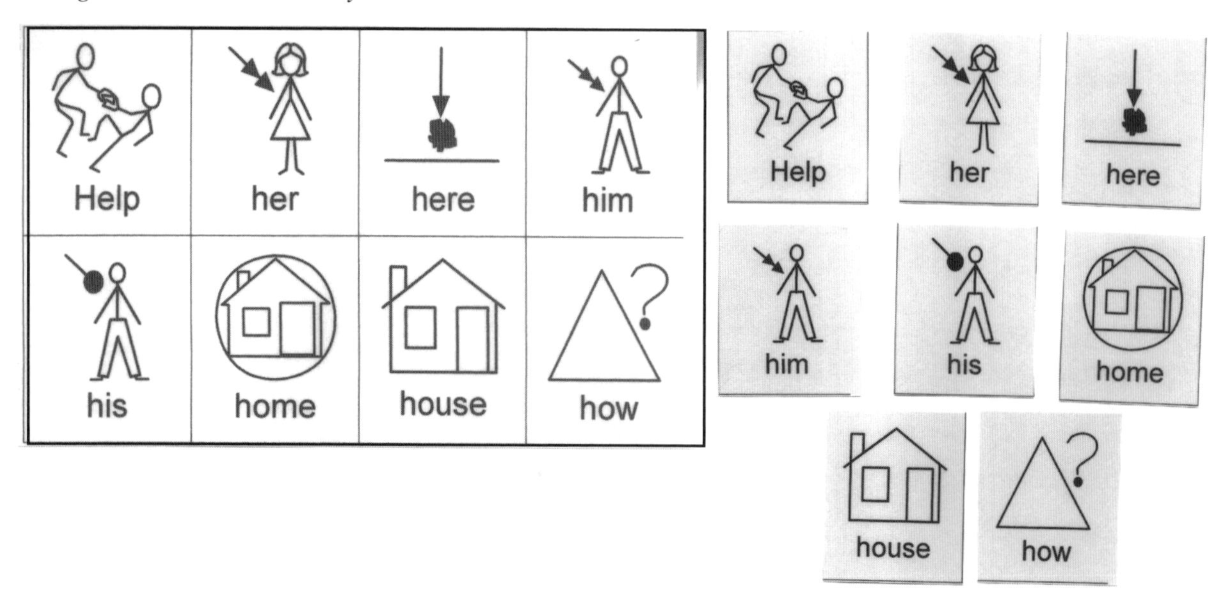

## Emergent literacy and symbols

➤ Jo Amstutz and her colleagues at St John's school have created books of short stories in symbols for her pupils. The stories are designed to reflect the age and interests of her students. Many of the ideas have come from the students themselves, and have been illustrated with various drawings and clip art. The stories are about children's experiences, such as picnics, discos and camping, as well as more imaginative ones.

*Cover and title of one of the story books created by a teacher for her pupils.*

➤ At Wilson Stuart School, Dave Wood has worked on many literacy support strategies. For example, when making reading books, pages can be protected by inserting them in plastic envelopes in a ring binder, however, the glossy ones can be hard to read. Dave has also been creating symbol dictionaries.

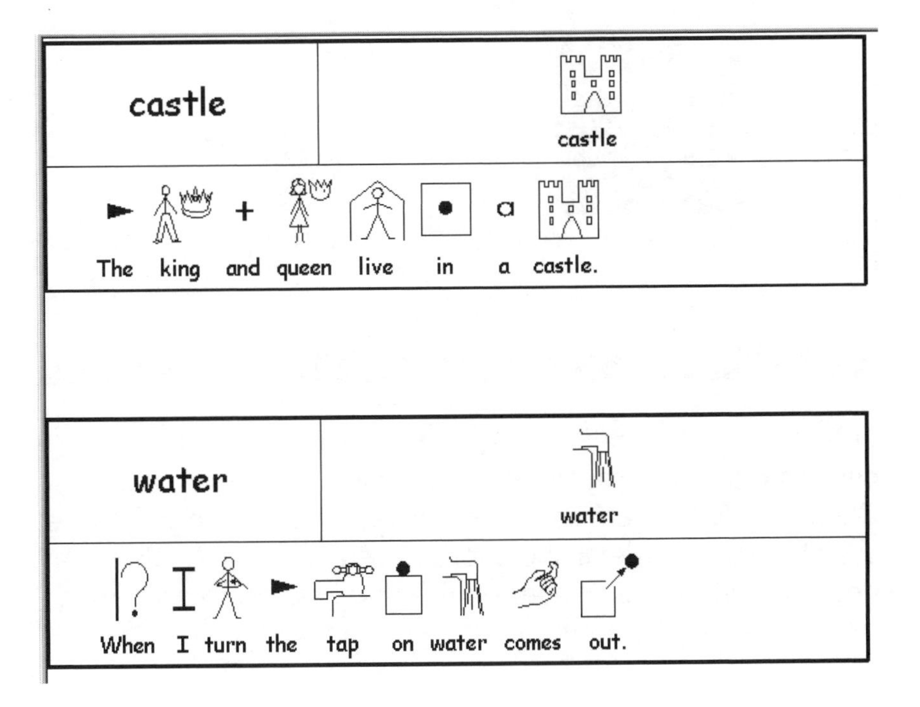

➤ Charlotte is a young symbol user who has used a symbolised text about her life at school. As usual, photographs are shown alongside word and symbol captions, but in this case a flap has been placed over each photograph. This means that Charlotte can try to read the symbol and text line before lifting the flap to check from the photograph that she is correct. Charlotte's class teacher at the time was Leo Berry, from the Lambert School. Each of the children in the class made such a book. Not only did it make relevant and motivating reading material for the author, it also makes books which are of interest to their peers.

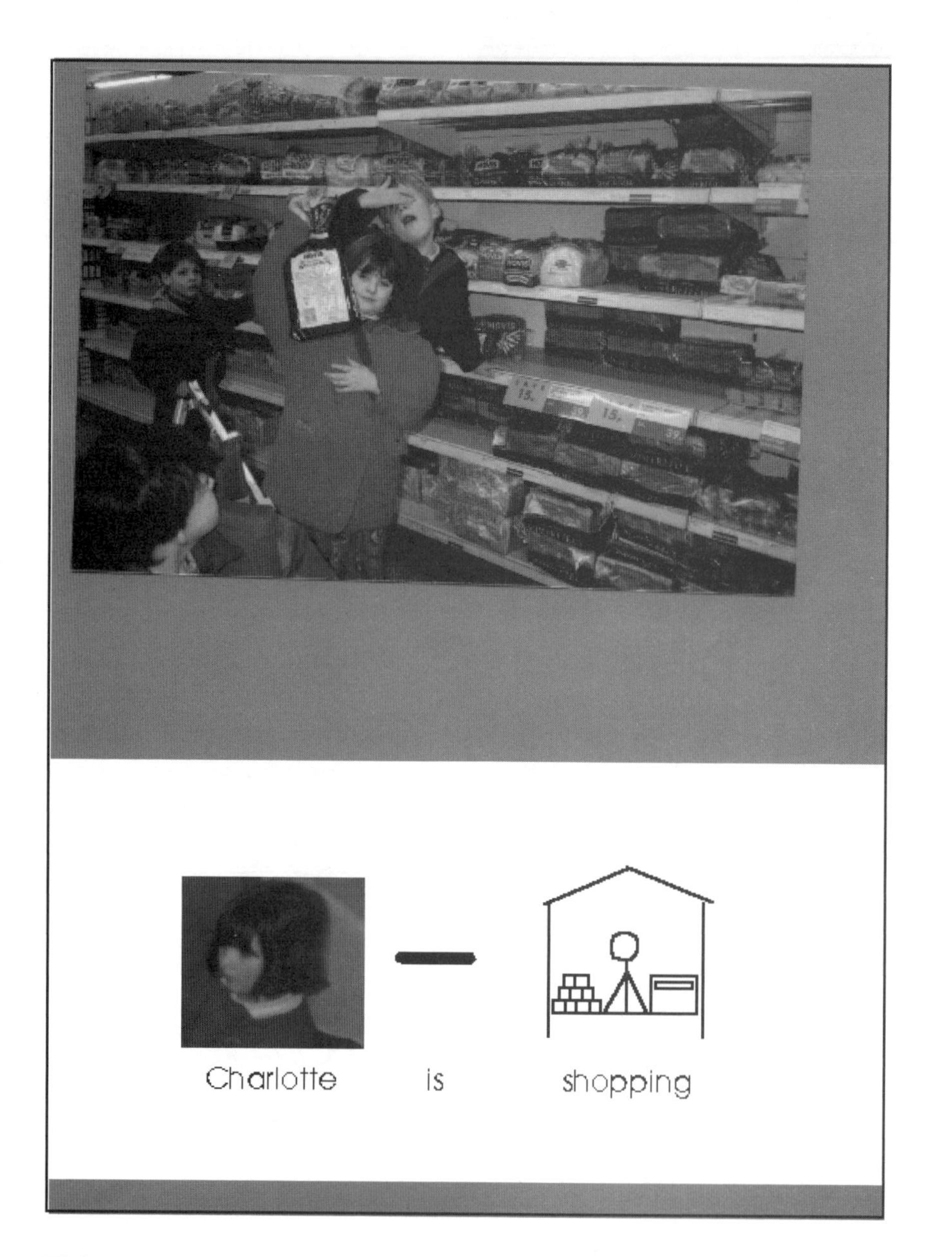


*A personal book using photographs and symbol captions makes a relevant and interesting book for emergent readers.*

This technique of making books from pasted up items is quite common. It is the same technique used by Abigail, shown in Chapter 2. The writer can choose the pictures and the sentences, can choose the order in the book, and so even though they may need help with creating some of the elements, they can certainly be regarded as the authors.

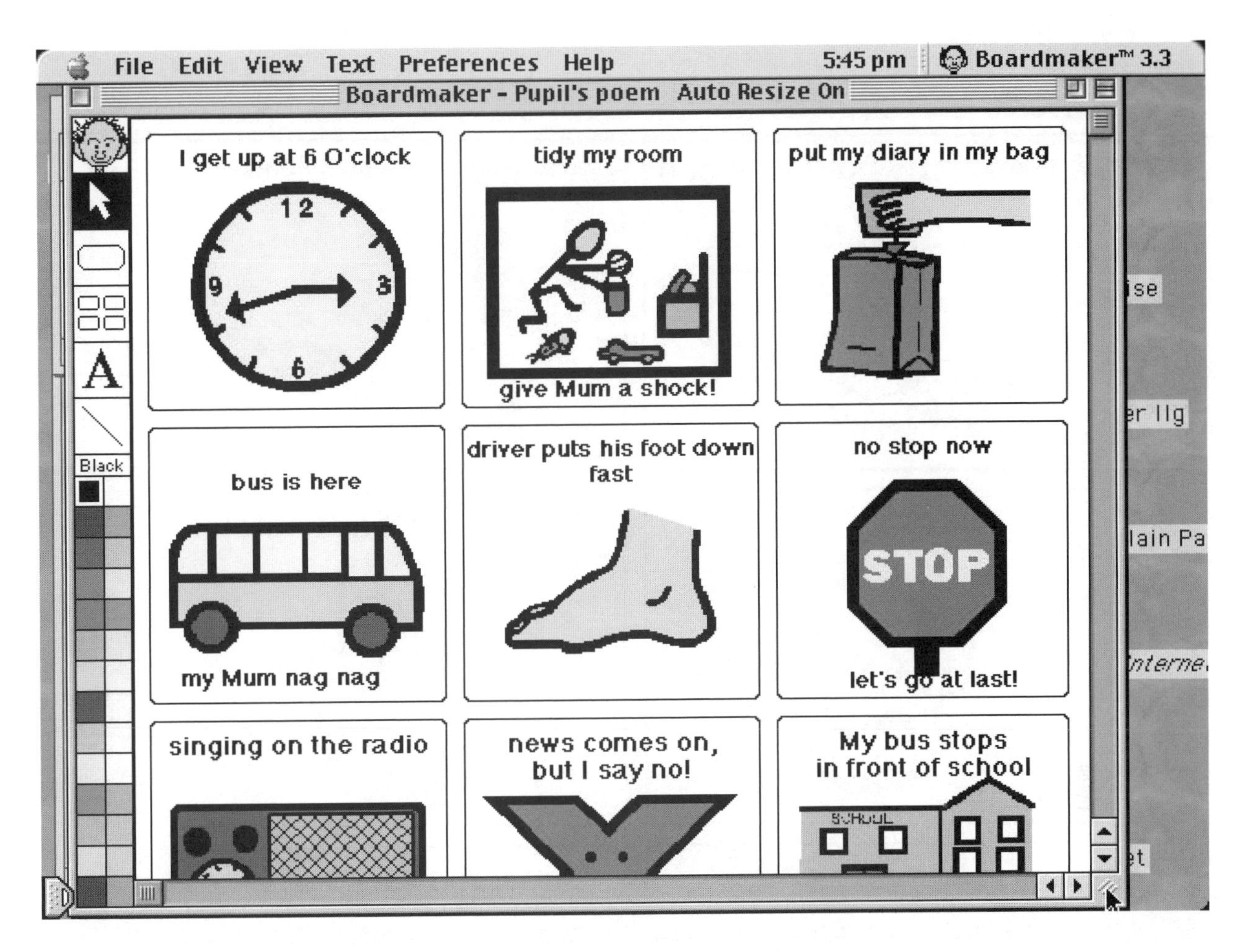


➤ These symbols are from BoardMaker, and used as a communication book for telling raps and poems. They are used by students at Frank Wise School. Sean O'Sullivan writes:

*Symbols on an overlay or communication board can be used for telling stories, building poems and for collaborative work as well as for individual functional communicaiton.*

> "Our pupils (with severe learning difficulties) might generally begin with physically separate symbols, and may progress to symbols printed out on grids for predictable situations. Beyond the grids we have actually found that our greatest use of the PCS symbols within BoardMaker has been to copy and paste into programmes such as HyperStudio or ClarisWorks. This allows us to make sure that the pupil using symbols can have just as much involvement in contributing to new class work as their peers. The symbols also of course mean that they can more readily understand the work, even if they do not make a direct contribution.
>
> Recent work at school has included making up a poem with symbols (both a "word-processing" version and a "multimedia" one), illustrating a corridor display on Aztec history (lots of blood and gore!) and using BoardMaker's multilingual ability to exchange information in symbols and photos with our Swedish link school, displaying the text in Swedish for them, and having checked it in English for us!"

*Different ways of exploring topics through poetry and raps using pre-designed boards or grids.*

## Summary

Symbols can open the door to literature for those who are unable to access it through text.

Symbols can be used to make resources, such as libraries, accessible to all.

Many people with autism find symbols helpful in everyday communication with others. Activities in the literacy hour can help to develop both communication and literacy.

Schools can use symbols as part of the literacy and numeracy frameworks.

Symbolised recording of student progress enables the student being assessed to share in the record that has been kept.

# CHAPTER 8

## CONCLUSION

This book celebrates a wealth of different practice, and has shown symbols enhancing learning, independence and communication. It should be clear by now that using symbols is not a simple process and that there are many issues which need to be understood if symbol use is going to be more than a token attempt to be inclusive.

There are two distinct types of application. The first is the situation where symbols appear singly, as in timetables and notices. These symbols can be explained and agreed with the user to represent complete ideas. It is not necessary to consider grammar or language structures. The main considerations are the choice of symbol, the presentation and layout, and most importantly, how the symbols are taught to the user.

The second situation is where symbols are included in sentences, both by staff creating materials for symbol readers and where users are constructing written material themselves. In this case there are additional considerations to be addressed. These involve the means of access to vocabulary, the range of symbols available and the technicalities of writing using the computer.

The case studies in this book have made clear not only the wide range of symbol use but also the breadth of purpose to be found. Also to be celebrated, of course, are the numerous individuals, whether their work is described here or not, who have brought their wit, invention and understanding to their interactions with symbol users enabling them to communicate and become more variously literate.

### The range of symbol use

It is as well at this stage to summarise the wide range of symbol use that has been described. We considered first some of the widely differing purposes for symbol use. We saw symbols providing a record of events to help users' recollections, and we saw them used in adult settings to promote safety and autonomy. We saw people with learning difficulties being helped to make decisions through their use of symbols, and we noted also their use of sequences of symbols to illustrate a series of events. We shared evidence of symbols as a lifeline communication within families, and for extending that communication outwards to schools and other agencies.

We then moved on to consider issues of vocabulary, consistency and understanding. We recognised that consistent use of symbols in different settings is very helpful to users, and that periods of transition, such as primary to secondary school, may be eased by liaison on symbol use. On the other hand, we also recognised that some users may be much better suited to their own personalised symbol set, or by one which uses modifications of existing symbols. The paramount issue throughout is that we should ensure that the user and others understand. It is only then that symbols can truly enable, for example, people with learning disabilities to understand a range of choices and express a preference.

Communication is a key purpose for using symbols, and we noted that such use is often related to individual needs rather than to specific systems. Some of those specific systems, however, have been developed in localities to meet a range of needs, and much of this development has been fuelled by the rapid increase in symbol technology, especially through the use of symbol software. This is linked to the area of online resources, an important issue for the next few years as this sector expands rapidly. Understanding the need for appropriate screen displays should be borne in mind by designers of online content if their resources are to be available for all. Symbols have a role to play in many different communication systems, and we would expect that the variety of such settings will continue to increase.

We turned then to the use of symbols for accessing information. We noted the benefits for users of information in symbol format and the effects on autonomy. Many resources may be symbolised in order to make them available to as wide a group as possible, but care will need to be taken to ensure that the symbols chosen are as widely accessible as possible.

Inclusion was a central focus for the next group of case studies, and we noted that inclusion is an aim not just for schooling but for the workplace and the wider community. Within the workplace, symbol use can help workers to become more productive, and they can be vital in including users in ceremonies or life transitions. We also found that symbols can provide prompts in self-advocacy contexts and can help users to make full use of services, including the opportunity to provide feedback.

Finally, we considered the area of literacy and literature, topics central to schooling but also important throughout life. We saw that symbols have been used to make literature accessible to those who cannot access it through text, and that some of this work has developed through the National Literacy Framework. We explored the particular case of the use of symbols by people with autism, and we addressed the important issue of user involvement in assessment through symbol use.

## Issues

This book, then, has explored a wide variety of contexts within which symbols are assisting users to communicate, choose, be literate and be included. Of course, there are many other issues that need to be addressed as we move forward in our use of symbols.

Many older adults have missed out on the educational opportunities that are now, thankfully, being offered to their younger counterparts. These adults may only now be developing a sense of autonomy and symbols can assist in this process. In many cases, the symbol use may be developed through a total communication system; their importance is as part of a holistic programme rather than as an isolated technique. Many of the other communicative technologies, such as computers or television, share some of the benefits of symbols, especially if their use is planned in a group context. Symbol software has done much to assist and support the integration of many different communicative systems, and the convergence of technologies such as the computer, telephony and television over the next few years will see such software migrating to different platforms. We can only wonder at the future possibilities that might exist for a symbol-supported Internet-linked digital television.

In reviewing current practice, certain key themes have emerged, which should inform further development:

### Concensus

There is no national consensus on the use of symbols in the UK and perhaps there never will be, but there is a need for a national debate and a developed awareness of the issues. This book is designed to be part of that debate.

Over the last five years there have been a number of articles and events exploring symbol use. These have shown widespread enthusiasm for an extension of symbol use, provided that certain factors are borne in mind. One of these factors was the lack of recorded practice on which to base development and it is hoped that this book will be a small step in that direction.

### Training

Training will be essential if inappropriate use is to be avoided. Training is needed for people who are creating symbols materials as a source of information for non-text readers. Guidelines developed through practice need to be shared to ensure appropriate use of English.

Care will need to be taken in the use of symbol software; although the programs are, quite rightly, easy to use, their use needs to be informed by an understanding of the issues involved in symbolised communication.

### Symbol choice and development

We need to understand the nature of the symbols we use with the individual. The consensus from the contributors to this book is that it is not helpful to stick rigidly to a single symbol set, but to use images which are acceptable and understood by the individual. These images may come from a range of sources and will most likely include local or personalised symbols and photographs.

Symbol development needs to respond to the requirements of the users and their organisations. Where possible, users should be involved in the development of symbols and the environments in which they are used. Issues of copyright will need to be resolved as symbols migrate from care and school settings to the wider world of publishing and online resources, and it is most important that symbols are seen more widely in the environment.

### Management

Organisations need to consider the range of symbols they use, and adopt clear policies so that there is a measure of consistency amongst all users. It is evident from the examples throughout this book, that the extent of symbol use and its quality is significantly enhanced by management support. Symbols are more likely to be embedded in daily practice when it is supported by organisational management

### Research

Most of evidence on the use of pictorial symbols is anecdotal, such as in this book. There is a need for more structured and rigorous evaluation, which can inform the development of coherent policies locally and more broadly.

There is little published research into the transparency of pictorial symbols, and much of the evidence upon which current thinking is based is anecdotal. There are quite large numbers of small-scale studies carried out by post-graduate students on modular courses as part of their personal development, but there is no mechanism at present for sharing these studies. These papers tend not to be written up for academic journals or for dissemination in less formal ways, and a forum is required in which these discussions can be carried forward.

**Sharing practice**

A symbol email forum was set up at the request of delegates at one of the Meldreth Manor School/Widgit Symbol conferences with this objective. However, it seems to be the general experience of email forum users that the majority of members prefer to view other's contributions rather than participating actively. The result is that a small number of people share increasingly technical discussion, rather than entering into more in-depth debate. It is arguable that the nature of email communication, which more usually features short sharp pieces, is not appropriate to the type of discussion required.

Conferences are perhaps a more useful means of extending these debates, for example the very valuable and enlightening 'Power Through Symbols' conference, organised by the New Possibilities Health Trust in 1999 raised and debated many issues relating to symbol use. The main limitation of such conferences is that the debate cannot be shared with a wide audience. Conference reports tend to be conveniently short rather than reflecting the quality of thought behind the discussion.

There is a need for some focused and rigorous research into key issues on symbol practice. There is also a continuing need to exchange ideas through formal and informal means, to identify even more practice, and to develop practical guidelines and training.

What this book clearly shows is that there is a large number of people using symbols successfully, thinking through these issues, and developing good practice in their own organisations: the challenge is to share this. This book has started the process: now it's over to you.

# Appendix

Very many people have sent contributions to this book. We have drawn on a large selection of these. There were simply too many to fit in. We have drawn on materials and ideas from the following people and organisations. We appologise sincerely for any errors or if we have omitted anyone from the list. With so many materials, this was always a possibility.

| | |
|---|---|
| Carol Allen | Hadrian Education Centre, Tyne & Wear |
| Jo Amstutz | St John's School, Brighton |
| Terry Aylen | Croydon MENCAP |
| David Banes | AbilityNet, Reading |
| Stephanie Baines | ECHO, Leominster |
| Keith Bates | Pathway Employment Services, North Finchley |
| Leo Berry | The Lambert School, Stratford-upon-Avon |
| Sheryn Biggs | Ivers College, Dorset |
| Mrs J Billingham | Sandside Lodge School, Cumbria |
| Tiffany Birch | Nash College of FE, Bromley, Kent |
| Nicola Brodie | Kensington & Chelsea College, London |
| Erica Brown | Acorns Children's Hospice, |
| Ian Burtenshaw | St Piers School, Surrey |
| Karen Burton | Hollacombe Community Resource Centre, Devon |
| Susan Burnes | Parent |
| Ros Chapman | Independent consultant |
| Jacqui Clark | News 4 You, Cincinnati, USA |
| Stuart Concannon | Parents |
| Jo Coulson-Davis | RAD, Surrey |
| Morag Correa | Woodcroft School, Essex |
| Justin Drew | Glebefields Health Centre, Sandwell, Birmingham |
| Linda Edwards | St Piers School, Surrey |
| Jo Egerton | Sunfield School, Clent |
| Diane Ellingham | Glenvale School, West Bromwich |
| Ray Elliott | Elleray Park school, Wirral, Merseyside |
| Cath Farr | Downsview School, Brighton |
| Nicci Forshaw & Vicky Roberts | Brooklands Communication Team, Birmingham |
| Tracy Fowler | Norton Radstock College, Radstock |
| Johanna Frohm | Parent |
| Gela Griffiths | Redbridge High School, Liverpool |
| Nichola Grove | City University, London |
| Bernard Gummett | George Hastwell School, Cumbria |
| Anne Hancox | Worcestershire NHS Trust |
| Marc Hooker & Julie Sullivan | MENCAP |
| Ann Hyde | MENCAP Development Worker |
| Julie Keen | Lea Castle Centre,Wolverley |
| Lucy Kilbride | The Children's Society, York |
| Theresa Latham | SE Essex College |
| Pete Le Guys & Karl Seymour | Real Voice Media, Bristol |
| George and Eileen Lindley | E & G Publications, Cumbria |
| Gill Lloyd | Woodlands School, Surrey |

| | |
|---|---|
| Maureen Lyme | Ravensbourne NHS Trust, Farnborough Kent |
| Ann MacLellan | Parent |
| B Maidlow | Marlborough Day Service, Wiltshire |
| | Mandeville School, Northolt |
| Julie Marples | The Holway Centre, Somerset |
| Wendy Marriott | Parent |
| Alison Matthews | The Learning Disability Service, Oldham |
| Anne McKehty | Northfield School, York |
| Judy Melland | .... (See Wendy MArriott) |
| Mrs Lisbeth Meek | Chailey Heritage School, Lewes |
| Maggie Morgan | Forum & Greenwich Community Centre, Greenwich |
| Lyn Morris | Grimsbury Park School, Bristol |
| J Mulholland | Parent |
| Anne & Alan Nelson | Parents |
| Andrew Nicholls | Hounslow Self Advocacy Project |
| Sue Norton | Deerswood Special School, West Sussex |
| D O'Connor | Fullerton House School, Doncaster |
| Anne O'Loughlin | Grimsbury Park School, Bristol |
| Janet O'Sullivan | Moorfield School, Preston |
| Sean O'Sullivan | Frank Wise School, Oxfordshire |
| Micléle Page | Watergate School, Lewisham |
| Sara Pells | Heathside School, Suffolk |
| Scott Pickard | Queen Elisabeth II Jubilee School, London |
| Debbie Rai | NE Wales NHS Trust, Wrexham |
| Nicole Rappell | Lord Mayor Treloar Specialist FE College, Alton Hants |
| Claire Richards | The Bridge, Leatherhead |
| R P Richards | Carer |
| Clive Robertson | Dilston College, |
| Nic Rowland-Crosby | Devon Total Communication, Learning Disability Service |
| Mrs Julie Russ | Cheshire Foundation Housing Asociation |
| Jos Sels | Het GielsBos, Belgium |
| Yasmin Shah | Bradstow School, Broadstairs Kent |
| Char Smith | Devon Total Communication, Learning Disability Service |
| Jackie Stubbs | New Possibilities NHS Trust, Colchester |
| | Toby Homes |
| Anne Turner | Glebe House project, IRALD, Leicestershire |
| Mandy Townsend | Mabel Prichard School, Oxfordshire |
| Jessica Tuck | OPAL, Oldham |
| Richard Walter | Meldreth Manor School, Royston Hertfordshire |
| Wendy Wardle | Ysgol Y Graig, Colwyn Bay Conway |
| David Ware | Little Heath School, Romford Essex |
| Wayne Wilson | Communication Aids Service, Colchester |
| Dave Wood | Wilson Stuart School, Birmingham |
| Judy Wood | Springfield School, Oxfordshire |
| Jane Young & Bev Vaughan | Isle of Wight College |